Seed

JOANNA WALSH

NO ALIBIS PRESS

This edition published in 2021
by No Alibis Press
Belfast

Printed and bound by TJ Books Limited, Padstow

Cover design and typesetting by Stephen Connolly
Illustrations by Joanna Walsh

ISBN 978-1838108106

Cold Pastoral!

—John Keats, *Ode on a Grecian Urn*

No future

—Sex Pistols

May

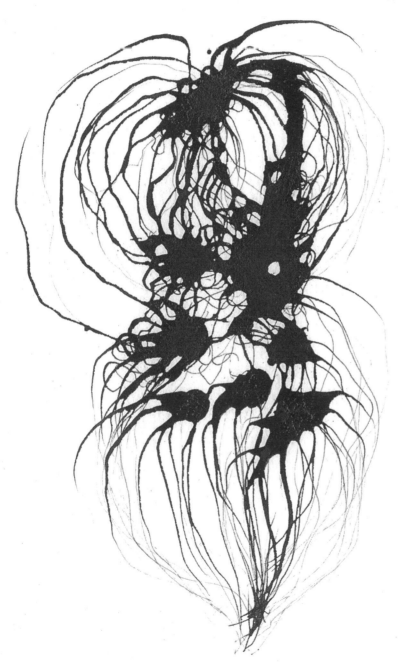

Opening

I must stop doing it.

In the fields the yellow spreads across. It is inauthentic.

When I open the cages at the cattery this cat goes to the side of the wall. This cat tries to bite me. There are two cats in this cage.

They eat kitekat. 'They come here, they eat all sorts of things. When they leave, they eat kitekat.'
This is what the owner says.

The owner gives me the key, and walks back to her white bungalow at the top of the ridge.
I put my headphones on. I listen to Queen on tape. I can see the cats through their wire. They seem to move slower.
Her wide bottom in fawn stretch trousers. Nylon.
She has given me the keys. To the cattery, to the food bin. To the cat litter bin. I have a can opener.

Fields should be green.

The cattery is on a ridge. It looks over the yellow fields. Around the bungalow are conifers. They break the wind.
The cattery is 'exposed'.

They make it into margarine. I don't know when they harvest it.

I listen to Paul Simon. I can't get radio here.

(And yellow oil.)

The cattery is a low building. It is grey. In it there are two storeys of cages. Outside there are runs fenced round with chicken wire.

I notice when the hard balls of the hawthorn blossom come.
Each day I bicycle to the cattery.

I have two cassettes. Queen and Paul Simon. Queen played somewhere near here. They are English. Paul Simon is American. I can't see him ever.

(About a mile from my house.)

I have a walkman. The headphones have two parts. They slide against each other for carrying. The fit is not perfect. I slide them carefully. I do not over-slide them. When they hit home, they rattle.

The ridge looks over a valley. In the valley are yellow fields. At the bottom of the valley is a river.

I clip the walkman on my belt.
The sponge in my ears. I can feel the metal inside the sponge.

It is not a river. It is a stream.
At home I make a new mixtape.

I mean they're not cages. I don't know what else to call them.

I place the tape recorder as near as I can to the radio. They must both be plugged in. I can stretch it so they're twenty centimetres apart. The radio is a clock radio alarm. I switch on the radio and the tape recorder at the same time. The radio plays the top 40.

Enclosures?

When I started I didn't know the name for it. I thought it was just pretending something.

I look it up in the dictionary. It says self-abuse. I still don't know what that means.

I go to the cattery every day.
I'm only here for the summer.

Rosemary

There is no guarantee of anything.

Men came to the fields next to my house.
They are here to build new houses. They have a concrete mixer.

I can stand in the stream. On the floor of the stream are pebbles. The stream comes up to my ankles. In the middle, up to my knees. Sometimes the stream is higher, sometimes it is lower. This depends on lots of things. I don't know what these things are.
The water is very clear.

First the men put in sticks in the ground and strings between them. The next day they dig down in squares. The weather is dry but there are pools. I can't see their faces. I can't hear what they shout to each other, just the noise of shouting. It echoes off the sides of the valley. When they are done the estate reaches our house.

Rosemary comes to the stream with her sister.
Rosemary is my age.
Rosemary's sister is younger than her.

Sometimes the cats hiss at me. Sometimes they roll over to let me tickle them. I listen to Paul Simon, 'she's got diamonds on the soles of her shoes'.
At the end of May, young things!

When I think of Rosemary, I do not see her: something is hot and black. Her sister is smooth. She is thin, her skin is white with freckles. She has short hair. It is not too short, it is neat. Rosemary's sister plays tennis.

I work the morning shift. First I feed the cats, then I clean them out. I leave the key for the owner on top of the feed bin under a flower pot.

Rosemary's mother is clean but not decorative. She is folding something clean but with holes in.

I live outside the outskirts of town, between the village and the estate. It's not a place. It could scarcely be called a hamlet. You can't hear the ring road, but you can feel it. The ring road is close to my house. You can go under it.

By the underpass is a post tagged

S

E

X

Between the village and my house is the valley.

The pollen comes off the rape.

Rosemary lives on the estate on the edge of town. I don't live there. I live in a house with a damp cellar.

The cellar is dark. My parents want to use it for storage but it is too damp. They try to install lights but it is too damp. When we move into the house, I want to live in the cellar, but it is not possible. I go down into the dark of the cellar. After the bright my eyes see red.

Ducklings swimming oh obedient!
Rape in flower. That yellow, not the right yellow. No. Yellow is not that
half-green: poisonous.
Small frogs. That stuff called cuckoo spit that does look like spit frothy.
This is nature. I don't know nature. It means nothing besides what I live
every day.
The late-born ones don't survive the winter.

I go to Rosemary's house. It is white and thin. It staggers the other
houses at right angles. They are all in a row.
I begin to go there in the spring.
(Across the field, the combs of ploughing.)

Our cottage is old already. Once it was a butcher's shop, on its own
not with any other houses so I don't know whether to believe this. It is
faced with white pebble dash. Toward the bottom it is green, and the
pebble dashing is crazed. In front of the house is crazy paving. The front
door is glass, wrinkled. Once everything in it was red. When I think of
this the red covers my eyes.

Rosemary has an electric toothbrush.
Rosemary is going to Cambridge.
Rosemary's mother has a boyfriend.
Rosemary's mother is a sculptor.
(These are some sentences I do not understand.)

In our hall is the telephone, and the telephone table. They are next to the glass door. When I sit at the telephone table I can see if there is someone watching me, but I can't see who. The person outside can see I am there, but can't see my face. At the side of the house a patio door faces a hedge. Through the hedge is a field. That is where the men are working.

The hedge is stringy and thin.

Rosemary's mother wears glasses. I can't remember her body. I think it must be flat inside her clothes.

When our phone rings I go down to the hall. Before I answer it I look through the glass door to see if anyone is watching. When the post is delivered, the postman steps right up to the glass but I still don't know what he looks like.

Because her body is flat I think she must be a good person.

In through the telephone, in through the letterbox, come other people. I don't know what they look like. I cannot stop them.

Rosemary gets into the bath. She has bought a leather skirt second-hand. It is too big. She says she has heard if you wet leather you can shrink it. She can't get the skirt off after. And she laughs. And that's the best thing it's worth it to ruin the skirt to laugh like that. Or to see her laughing.

Our bathroom faces the field. It has a long window. I wash, but not my whole body. I wash my armpits, chest, face, with a flannel. If I stand by the basin the men can't see me through the window. The bath is below the window, the shower is in the corner beyond the window. They can't see me in the bath or the shower, though when I get out they can see me unless I crawl along the floor.

(Rosemary's mother speaks to me confidentially. She says Rosemary's sister suffers from cystitis.)

It is necessary to wring the flannel well so it does not drip on the floor, which is carpet.

(I say to Rosemary's mother, 'is that something to do with the nose?')

Downstairs, the catch on the patio door does not work sometimes. People come into the garden.

But then Rosemary's mother is not always at home.

The man who came into the garden. I was reading Hamlet.
I was sitting in the garden in defiance of what?
I was reading Hamlet for university.
He was a religious person. He had come to convert me.

When I stand in the stream I see Rosemary, hot and dark. My toes clutch the pebbles. They are sharp but clutching makes it more controlled. The feeling goes right up between my legs.
I saw myself sitting there in the garden.
I had been waiting for someone to come into the garden.

He has not come again.

The stream is also very cold.

I have not been to the university. I filled in a form and I got the place. The notice came through the letterbox by the glass door. The letterbox is vertical.

I am going there in October.

I did well in my exams, but still I don't know anything.

Sound

This is everything I know about the valley:

(A grass whistle makes the loudest sounds.
This can be doubled.)

If you shout from the ridge it bounces off the far side of the valley.

But if you stand by the bridge at the bottom of the valley you don't hear it.

If you shout from the bridge it bounces off both sides of the valley.

If a car comes down the valley you hear it from the bridge before it gets there, before you hear most cars.

It works the same from the other side of the valley but we never go there.

(That ridge down the middle of the grass interferes if you want to whistle. If you want to whistle better pick a flatter, weaker blade. Or a larger blade and split the blade in half.)

It is necessary to walk down to the stream at the bottom of the valley. You can do that via the road or through the fields.

Some things tickle but make sure they're not nettles.

Things that are not nettles can still feel sharp.

To walk through the fields is more authentic. Because it is not concrete.

(There are also some leaves you can pick with a flat wide stem that is thick. If you snap the end without breaking, and pull it back against itself, strings leave the stem about five of them or maybe even more, and follow the snapped-off piece. As with the grass juice comes out.)

In the fields it is difficult to walk on the hardened furrows.
If you walk between them you get dust in your shoes.

(This is called making telephone wires.)

Plimsols smell, but the dust gets into the sandals quicker.
If you get dust between your toes in sandals, it rubs into tiny worms.
You can pick them off later.

(Also, you can take one of the leaves on a clover and split it without taking it off the plant and fool people that it's a four-leaved clover. The green gets under your nail, and also round the cuticle. Your hands smell green.)

I am really quite ignorant. Still I have preserved myself in nature.

In the summer you can smell green all the time even sometimes in the house. Sometimes in the kitchen, drains.
I can almost smell it, the green, even when I'm not in the valley. It's like knowing half a word.

Baby

I take it from the chemist's shelf below the lipsticks and slip the bottle, which is small and flat as a toffee disc, into my pocket.

Nobody sees. It is called Love Musc.

I only have one chance to tell this tale.

I walked towards the executive estate on the other side of the plantation. The road is a narrow country road. There is no pavement. On either side hedges to 8 feet. Behind me each car slows.

I pass

S

E

X

It was winter but the trees are still thick. They are pines. They have grown up quickly to enclose the executive estate. I see myself living here one day. Some boys pass in a 4 x 4. They drive into the executive estate. I see myself married to them. All of them? Any of them.

Why? Because they are rich.

I have bought a charm with a small red stone. I put it on a necklace. It is a charm I have seen a teacher wear. It is a six-pointed star. I bought it from a head shop in town.

I don't know what it means.

I have never been more than ten miles from here.

I babysit on the executive estate. The man is going to the Rotary Club. He is going with his wife. It is a dinner. I ask if she is a member of the Rotary Club too. He says women are not allowed to be members. I ask him why. He says it is because the club is for business men. He said there are no business women in this town so there is no need for women to be members. Because there are no business women the fact that women cannot be members does not matter. The man and his wife go out. I am wearing Love Musc.

It is not often hot here: when it is, the landscape is different.

The man's lounge carpet is deep and cream-coloured.

The man's dog is big and black. It is a boy dog. I play with it. After some time I lie on the floor and pull my skirt up. The dog sniffs me. Its cock extends long and orange. I get frightened and sit on the sofa and watch TV.

The man returns from the dinner. I leave. The man gives me a record. It was the Bonzo Dog Doo-Dah Band. I play it on my turntable, looking at the sunset. The window in my bedroom faces the sunset.

After work, I see Rosemary and her sister. Rosemary is hot and dark. Her sister stretches her limbs, then folds them. They are long and white. We sit on the bridge. Rosemary goes under the bridge.

No, wait! When I babysit and the man and his wife return from the dinner, the wife goes into the kitchen. The man gets my coat. At the door the man opens his mouth on mine. It is full of smoke. It is as good an initiation as any.

Nothing actually happens. We are not sinister people. Girls do not contain within themselves that which cannot be said about them.

(OK, sometimes we smoke cigarettes.)

The man does not ask me to babysit again.

I do not know if he can have known what I had done. Instead I get the job at the cattery.

Green

I bike to the cattery in the morning.

There are white butterflies, or are they moths? They have green veins like the leaves.

The cow parsley smells blunt. I put my hand on it once, pulled it up, trying to pick it, it is so pretty, but the next day my palm comes up in blisters from the raw juice. There are two kinds of cow parsley. Don't touch the kind with thick stems, and short hairs like blonde leg stubble. I cut my ankle shaving once. It bled so bright red I was frightened. In the shower the water ran red too and the colour didn't get weaker. The blisters are purple and juicy. I slide a pin into them because I've been told to. The blood is a different colour. But what's inside's clear water.

If you break the cow parsley inside it is hollow with small hairs and some clear wet.
(The insides of my body different in different places.)

Thistles. Also the ones hidden in between the wheat. Ragwort. Yellow. Also that stuff by railway tracks. Purple. What is it? Loosestrife. Both are weeds.

And.

The spikes, I don't know what they're called, about 20cm the stalk green faceted with a long fat thing on the top made of dark pods. Not black, there is no black in nature. Round the black dark brown whatever a halo of white. Look closely and they're joined by threads. It's the way they feel when you pull your fingers up the stalk, encircling then the fat bit that explodes in all directions. pods. A halo of white round the top unless you don't look closely. Oh yes they're called plantains.

Stalks in nature are always thicker than you think. And with veins going all the way up. You can rip them out. And soft in between. Pulpy. It is May. Winter becomes a handful of silly anecdotes. In the stream ducks rape each other, well, the males.

In the stream reeds that cross each other. They're green part of the way brown at the bottom. The brown parts like a husk. How do they keep on growing if they're brown?

In the stream horsetail stalks in sections. At each section some hairs, a ridge. Why? This evidence of their growing for what?

And at the beginning, the horse chestnuts are bearing something. They call them candles. With a flick of pink at the top, orange almost (the dog's cock, unexpected).

Cowslips those are pretty flowers that people recognise they resemble flowers in vases. You don't see them so often in the wild mostly green things with joints like limbs thick and juicy or that do some bad things like sting you or aren't very recognisable just green or are bad considered weeds. Sometimes as a surprise flag iris just like something on purpose growing in a garden.

Spring flowers are yellow: buttercup, iris, horsetail. Rape.

Then there is daffodil which is earlier, but I only see that in parks.
Daffodils are not natural.
Rape is not natural.

What do they put on the fields so that between the stalks no weeds?
They spray it.

I bike to the cattery breathing in only three times.

Stream

When we first come to the stream me and Rosemary and Rosemary's sister the water is one two feet high. Very small fish congregate around the wooden posts that go down into the water.

The boy in my class was wearing a t-shirt. It says The Smiths. I know something about who they are but I don't know. There is no way to know. My dad buys a newspaper. It says nothing about them. The radio plays pop. It's local radio, but it's not from around here. It is local because it is also played in the pubs the houses the shops the discotheques. I do not know how this t-shirt gets onto this boy but I know something of what it must mean. It means the possibility of something different. The boy had white hair. It was vertical. It means the possibility of something different. Underneath his white hair he was white. Everyone at my school is white.★

The water flows off the sprayed land.

★When I say 'everyone was white' I mean almost everyone. Maybe about three people weren't.

The water flows away from the village toward the estate.

Some people in the VIth form can drive.
The bridge is the road. It is made of concrete. It does not go up in a hump like pictures of bridges.

You can tell it is a bridge only because of the stream underneath it, and because of the wooden posts on each side.

It is good to be multicultural. This is what we are taught at school. There are pictures of people on posters in the library being multicultural together. It is good but we don't have that here. We sit underneath the posters. We are white. There is nothing we can do about it. On Fridays sometimes my family eats Chinese. Sometimes we eat curry sauce on fish and chips. I prefer pie. Sometimes we just eat normal food, which is a disappointment. Here we don't have the option of being good.

In winter the river floods. Cars cannot cross the valley.

On one side of the bridge is the cattery my house the estate then the town.

Beyond the bridge are other villages.

My parents do not drive on that side of the river. I have biked there sometimes. It takes a long time to get to any of them.

They are the real country.

*I cannot drive. I cannot drive far from people who are white.***

The concrete is hot. No cars come ever. We lay down in the road, me and Rosemary and Rosemary's sister.

*(**Which means a few aren't. I see them from a distance, but I don't even know their names.)*

The valley bounces sound.

We had a Pakistani boy in our class once, but only for six months. I dared not speak to him before he was gone.

I was preparing to.

If a car comes we can hear it turn at the top of the valley.

Nothing is from around here. The boy with white hair was in my history class. Even he came from the school next door. After the exams I don't see him again.

If we don't hear it in time the cars get us.
What was my interest in the white haired boy?

(Should I call them boys now, or men?)

Super

The supermarket by the ring road.

I got pre-sliced because it was cheaper. It's all the same isn't it?

Roesmary's mother puts it in the bread bin. *Let's eat that later.*

Daisies only grow outside nature. On the school field and on our garden when my dad mows it. He mows it a lot so the grass is always short. Never in the valley, not even by the side of the road.

Pulling the flowers from the gardens all along the road. Nobody in at this time of day. By the end of the road, a bouquet for Rosemary. One from each garden. Shake the water drops off, so it looks like a real bouquet. The beads on the flowers are round, magnify what's underneath them; the spots the tiny imperfections also the grain of the petals like skin. They're eyes. When they get onto me they're just wet. I got caught once, picking the head of a Chinese lantern at the bottom of the road through to the estate. The man ran after me and said are these your flowers then? I said no because they weren't but they were on the road side of the fence I didn't say that.

Fruits in the supermarket. They're a different species. Those strawberries all white in the middle all the year round, the crunchy peaches. Everything so shiny. Not a speck of earth anywhere. Why would there be? It goes straight from the grey shed to our formica kitchen. Once cut my mother wraps it in cling film and puts it in the fridge.

The Chinese lanterns' veins my gran's eyelids. If you put a light inside you can see it through it looks red in like when you close your eyes against the sun but you're looking at it from the inside.

One day no one knows cowslip sedge horsetail plantain willow.

When I arrive we make tea.
But we do not make tea for everyone.

I eat the French stick and jam and butter then I take another piece then another. Rosemary says it takes 20 minutes before the food hits your stomach you know. I know that means *don't eat any more* so I try to stop eating it but I am hungry. I should have brought more bread there's not enough for two.

It's cold inside the supermarket I draw in on myself I can see the goosebumps on my legs with the little hairs standing up they're red my legs with the pimples white the basket's cold also it's difficult to remember what outside's like.

Touch

Sometimes I come to the cattery early in the morning. The cats don't know the time.

In front of the cattery the grass is wet. It's wet every morning of course. The lawn is dense as astroturf. There are no weeds in it.

Spiders. I cross a lot of them in the morning. I don't like the feel, but I am sorry to break them.

They are called lacewings: the insects with green veins.
I am worried there is something wrong here.

Wash your hands at the end of the cattery session.
Cinquefoil, forget-me-not, marsh orchid. Sorrel, red clover, quaking grass.
Wear the yellow rubber gloves for clearing out the litter trays. Wash your hands after.
A gunshot. The noise of the automated scarecrow.
Wear the pink rubber gloves for clearing out the food trays. Wash your hands after.
The hawthorn blossom gone, the bramble blossom gone.
Wear the orange rubber gloves for putting the new food in. Wash your hands after.
Yellow rattle.
Then the pigeons start that noise. It means heat. It strokes me. All day.

Ragged robin a canker, looks like something ill.
Outside the cattery don't touch animals ever.
Brimstone butterflies.
The smell of humans on them doesn't go away.
Crowsfoot. Yellow things.
Birds neither.
They die, abandoned.

June: buttercups, silverweed, horsetail. I know the names. What does calling them do?

There are swallows. Sometimes they dip in the river. Or house martins. The birds at the moment are very small. They have adolescents with them. Some of the elderflowers have four stamens, others have five. Is that anomaly or something else? Is there something wrong here?

What happens to the cow parsley? The flowers die. Then there are small pods, flat, with a brown flat seed inside them that looks like a piece of dirt. You can slit your thumbnail down and open them up. I don't know why they have that dirty bit round the edge, I mean I don't know why nature would have that. It looks like the beginning of decay.

Nothing I know matters.
(Sometimes I like that.)

Art

You can hear the doves all the time in our garden, under the sycamore. I don't like sycamores. They're ubiquitous. There must be better trees. Sycamores can't be right. In town there are chestnuts and also those trees with small spiky balls on them that grow soft and green in pairs like hair bobbles. The doves in our garden say something else no they say *somewhere else* from their tall perspective looking down on lawns mowed with stripes, somewhere nature isn't the same kind we have round here.

In Rosemary's mother's house Rosemary's mirror. A dressing table set. A kidney. That sort with a skirt, a ballet skirt round it. The mirror gilt and white, white with the gilt knocked off. Her dressing table white, old white a bit yellow like teeth the skirt around it lilac underneath it's only chipboard.

If you lie under it you can see.

We are outside both in skirts no tights in our garden under the sycamores, the cold grass folded under Rosemary's knees too.

Rosemary says to me, *what's your ideal underwear?*

I say, *white, really plain, cotton, but white all the time. Not the kind that goes grey.*

This is not what I am wearing.

She says, *colours. I like to mix and match.* She says, *what's your ideal hairstyle.* I say, *I don't know just so it always looks good and I don't have to do much with it.*

In Rosemary's mother's house downstairs a doll, I mean a full-grown doll a mannequin that's what they call them, no arms no legs no wig, her lower half draped in a skirt her breasts bare. A green hat with a feather, a red Venetian mask. Tho their house is just like all the others I'd never been anywhere like it before.

Who are these grown-ups allowed to pretend?

When we got up our knees and lower thighs were the colour of boiled ham and had the shapes of many crossing grass blades printed on.

Rosemary's mother's sofa is flower print. It is saggy with use. It was cream but it isn't now. Rosemary's mother doesn't care. She doesn't care and it doesn't matter. This is amazing! That we can sit on the sofa and it doesn't matter and drink tea and eat biscuits and it doesn't matter. Under my legs I can feel the strings from her sofa where it's worn through at the edge on the back of my knees.

In my house are two paintings. Or they are not paintings, they're pictures of paintings—flat, no texture. They are both in narrow gilt frames with the gold rubbing off like Rosemary's dressing-table mirror. They have glass on the front. One has a title underneath it is called rain steam and speed. It's a brown mess. I don't know what it's of. I try to put the words next to something: nothing fits. The other is a picture of a girl sitting looking at something, her face lit from the front. She's wearing something big and mushy on her head. It's blue perhaps some kind of hat. It's at the back of her head which looks uncomfortable how does she keep it on I can't see the details. There are ugly yellow lights in her hair the same colour as the ugly yellow of the flowers in her hand. By ugly yellow I mean a smeary dirty yellow. You don't see flowers that colour ever. Why is she holding a bunch of flowers sitting down? There is something green and curved behind her a wall I don't know why it's curved like that and the edge of it is gilt curly like the frame. Beyond it people very blurry like looking through glass. She's looking out at them I don't know why or why they are there all together. They seem to be moving about but not enough getting up and sitting down but I can't see on what. There are red and yellow marks on them that look like her flowers. Her mouth is open like she wants to say something but stops. She looks anxious even afraid. This is wrong I think. People don't have that look in paintings. Anger maybe or hate, big emotions, but not that no. I don't know what to call it. It is a moving toward something.

The mugs in Rosemary's mother's house have chips. Nobody minds. People can live like this. They can live like this and still have paintings on the wall. I thought you had to have the furniture before you got the paintings, that you only got real paintings when everything else is nice. That's how it works for everyone else. Rosemary's mother has real paintings. They look imperfect you can see little marks on them and brushstrokes. There's a drawing and the corner's torn off and there it is still framed.

My parents never talk about the pictures. I don't know where they got them from, or why. They're art, so they must be beautiful. I respect them because of that.

Before I envied the people with those houses that look just like they're

29

meant to: the fences white and the woodwork white even if that way of life was peeling and the window where the telephone's inside just where it's meant to be so you can see someone sitting there through the wavy glass talking on the telephone just like they should be and carpets just like they should be in the hall and all the way up the stairs.

Now I envy Rosemary. But I don't know why.

My parents' two pictures are exactly the same size.

Fish

Each day I cycle to the cattery. A hare very early in the morning once. Rabbits always at dusk.

At the stream we catch the fish, me Rosemary her sister. We bring jars and scoop up the fish. It is so embarrassing to be so strangely old-fashioned that, as we are doing it, we pretend we are not. I worked the goldfish stall at the school fair once: orange live meat the struggling against fingers. I liked that feeling. It was secretly aliver than anything else.

The fish in the river are very small (the stream is very small).
Some of them are not fish they're going to be frogs.
Tiny flies hover above the stream surface especially at twilight.
No one fishes here.

I don't know anything about fishing. What do they do? Sit there with tobacco tins all alive inside orange and frightening. Then they use those things that are fake: a feather, or orange live meat. The stream is not the same as catching the goldfish for the school fair stall to put into bags for the winners. They were easy to catch, soft and fat I wanted to squeeze them.

There are cows in the field by the river now well cows in one bullocks only two in another separate so that:

I didn't squeeze them, just felt how it would be.

I have never seen animals fucking.
Though I have looked to see.

Crossing the field to the stream me Rosemary her sister, the cow head down or the bullock whatever it is head down not looking. We look at it /not look at it. If we don't look it won't look back. And if it does look…

The smell of dung the smell you're not supposed to but here it is we relish the not supposed to secretly something about it like bodies like something cooked.

Another thing moving there: a rabbit a moorhen a rat?

At which we run we run which brings the giggles when we giggle we feel that thing between our legs it stops us running almost it makes us go faster only on the spot tho we don't know what we want to happen.

Whatever happens it happens on one spot. That spot on us I mean as well as that spot in the field the field with the holes in it made by the cows bullocks whatever in wet weather where your leg can get caught and then you can't get any further and you're trapped and then and then.

We don't do it we just feel how it would be.

Is this what it is? Is sex fear?

WAIT!

WAIT, I have forgotten to describe myself!

I have a cream-coloured viscose shirt. It has an open neck and short wide sleeves. It has areas of bobbling under the arms slightly darker. I don't know if I should wear it tucked in or out.

My jeans are a middle boring colour.

On the whole I cannot remember the things I wear.

Clad.

I first see Rosemary's sister in her tennis clothes. Her shorts, thick white nylon with a crease (we are both synthetic), her arms long and thin like a boy's (they fold in), the hairs on her arms, long and dark. Along the side of her leg, the ridge and hollow of something. Her legs, thin but don't look thin. There is no other word for them, because they are thin but what is that word? Like a model, not thin but correct.

It was muscle.

Clad.

The branches clothed themselves instantly.
The ground rose waist high in nettles.
(You can't go any more between the trees.)

My jeans don't button the top button. I pull it across these white bits of me, and the white bits move. I am not a model, I can't work out which bits don't make me one. I can feel the top of the skin but the thickness between that and my bones, not. The button-back scars into the flesh. I am sorry I am an inconvenience.

When the hills, grass cut to chalk.
Clad.

My shirt sticking and I know there's a fold where my arm meets my shoulder not on top of course underneath I mean in the armpit it should be just a crease or even a hollow but there's too much there that's why I stick to sleeves even in the warm weather. I'm not what you'd call fat I'm the same weight as Rosemary we compared.

What do I call it, this wayward flesh?

The hills from far away look white.
Sometimes.
In the heat my body expands becomes less tight, the flesh now spongy does not do what I say but then I do not ask it very often.

I live beside it. I am no longer one thing.

We do not bother each other.

Sometimes I wear a pale blue skirt that gathers at the place my belly doubles.

My belly is pale and in the middle it folds. It is wrong.

Self-satisfied in my insignificance I am not thin but malleable. I fit the seats others find uncomfortable. I am unfailingly cheap. If I'm quiet

I can fit in with anyone. If I am very small perhaps Rosemary and her sister can condescend to spend some time with me.

My folding gives me satisfaction all the same. To feel it.

Rosemary's mother is flat. She folds something against herself with holes in. It is a tea towel.

Rosemary and her sister do not look sad their mother is divorced. We don't talk about it.

Rosemary and I and Rosemary's sister don't say things. We spend all our time not saying things. I remember these things, but I don't remember anything we said.

The stubble on my knees is intimate.

My knees taste of eggshells. After sitting with my knees up for a while I find my mouth is habitually over one of them.

I have read Chaucer.
I have never seen a pornographic magazine.

The backs of my knees stick to my thighs in the heat. I like to peel them off each other. It's easy: I just slowly straighten my legs. Through my blue skirt, the gravel embedded in my buttocks. It leaves little marks, red on red.

Everything said ties things up. I can't make an open-ended sentence. That's why I don't bother with sentences mostly.

But I can write a conversation with anyone. That's how I got a place at university. I don't know if I can use words for anything else. What use is my mouth? I can't even say this.

Things we do not talk about: Is there something wrong with Rosemary's sister? If we talk about it, that means it is true.

Just her build, perhaps. Or all that tennis.

I have read John Maynard Keynes.
I have never seen my mother naked.
I have never seen her cry.
My dad doesn't cry. Maybe no men do.

Rosemary's mother says *Rosemary, you must have heavy bones.*

Clad.

I know what happens to the hawthorn leaves.

Blue

They go to church on the telly.

The churches are in America. They are white clapperboard.

The church in the village is stone, I don't know how old that means. Its tower is square. It is grey.

The stone is flint. This is wrong. Flint is not stone.

Where we are is all flint and brick. I keep looking for the real England.

I have never been inside the church but I have seen it from the outside it is a tourist attraction they say.

(Who is they say?)

I go there with Rosemary and her sister.

The woman at the cattery does not come out ever not even when I lock up and leave.

Rosemary is waiting outside church.

Rosemary's dad is an 'entrepreneur'.

Rosemary's sister goes to a religious school.

Rosemary has to go to church for her sister.

I wear red gloves. They are lace.

I have bought a hat. It is camel.

(That's what it said on the label.)

It is correct to wear a hat in church.

(I know this from the telly.)

I am correct.

When I look up through the pale stained church glass the air is warped. This means the glass is really old. *In Rosemary's mother's house the window by the door is long and thin. The glass is wavy. This means you cannot see through clearly. Behind it is the telephone table.*

I furiously do not believe in god but out of respect, I have worn a black skirt and a black sweater.

Rosemary's mother's fence is white. It was built in the 1960s. This means the planks are horizontal. I sit picking the paint. I am waiting for Rosemary. It is hot.

There is a green hill far away without a city wall.

(I know all the words.)

I am still picking paint off the fence. It is not a wall.

I can remember anything that rhymes.

We sang them at school but it wasn't like church. There was nothing attached.

I mean they didn't mention all the rest. God, I mean. They didn't dare.

(Why does a hill have a wall?)

Rosemary's sister has a tennis lesson. I did not like to telephone beforehand.

Rosemary's sister is thin. Rosemary's mother is thin too but not like a model. She is flat. When I go to Rosemary's house we have tea. There is nothing else.

We do not bring the tea on a tray, with biscuits on a plate.

The tea is in chipped mugs.

I have heard the words before. On the telly. I can join in with some of them. Some of the hymns, we sang at school. I can remember all the words. I sing loudly.

Rosemary makes tea. This is novel. At home my mother makes tea. When Rosemary makes tea it is different.

My waist hurts like someone punches me at both sides. And there is the fizzing feeling, dehydration? No it is particular.

Rosemary's sister takes eucharist. She folds down neatly before the priest.

It is hot. My arms stick to the sides of my body. I feel liquid in my armpits.

I take the wafer into my mouth: it is a prawn cracker. It is a flying saucer. The sweet I mean. It is a very small thin piece of bread left on the breadboard overnight. But it is even. It sticks to my tongue. It tastes like skin. It dissolves.

I don't know what to do next.

The other people kneel on the kneeler so I kneel on the kneeler. The points of embroidery embed in my knees. *There is a scar on my knees. I came off my bike where there was new gravel cycling back from Rosemary's house.*

The gravel in the stream is sparse. There is mud between. It comes up around my toes. It gives. The gravel sharp. There may be other sharp things down there. The bible here is blue.

I have my period in the church. It is early. I can feel it bursting. I am kneeling on the kneeler. My skirt is made of corduroy. It is absorbent. I can feel the blood on my pants where it pools wet in the middle, also on my thighs. I feel it trickle down but not enough to show.

(While I feel this someone says a prayer.)

Few things are blue in nature. Some flowers.

We say the lord's prayer. I know it from school.
I pray fervently.
The blood on my thighs smells of rust. I can smell it from here.

The organ means everyone gets up. My tongue is dry. I rise and the colours become black. It starts at the top of my vision like smoke. I faint on the stone church floor. The small star charm on my necklace embeds its point in my chin. There is blood on my chin but it doesn't hurt. My waist hurts. I don't know the people who talk to me after. I try to feel they are not talking to me and I am not talking to them so I can leave more quickly. I sit on the step, they give me tea which I am not drinking and if I not-drink it quickly they can go away.

Rosemary and her sister are waiting outside all the time.

I cycled home I cleaned the cut up and stick on plasters. I cleaned the blood off my legs with a red face cloth. I said nothing to anyone.

What I do not say:
Both times I do not say anything about blood.

Red

Now I'm thinking about a red pot, a cooking pot, like for baking things in, like pies maybe.

It makes me think of being sick.

The opposite of red is green.

Inside is something brown baked on it smells of burnt fat. What is it? I can't quite remember.

Again there it is again the pot, red, at another point there is a split across it. It is clean. How did that happen?

Inside is brown, darker.

It's the glaze, a matt glaze.

I'm thinking about a red pot, a red pot. It is broken.

There was meat cooked inside it once, mince, I think.

I think I cooked it. I think I burnt the fat so it smelt bad.

It is clean now.

And it is broken.

I have forgotten what happened to it.

There is something about it that makes me feel like being sick.

Red is a danger colour in nature.

In school I go to the nurse's office and say I have a stomach ache. I hope she knows what I mean but she gives me paracetamol. I throw up. I lie on the bed—red leatherette—I am hot and something inside me feels hollow. It beats. I do not ask to go home. At the top of the nurse's office a tiny window thin along the top of the wall and outside it the top of those trees tied to sticks that are never fully grown, thrashing. It is red it makes me feel sick.

I am scared of this red jelly bag that sometimes gets heavier and fuller so full that it spills. It's so inconvenient it batters against my back, my belly trying to get out it asks to be mentioned but is unmentionable and it asks and asks again. I'd prefer it to all be over like to be an old woman—when does it stop? 50? 60?—Never to have the choice the need to mention or not mention this thing that asks and asks and that also provides the other unwieldy insistent things, all embarrassing that she carries around that means she needs a handbag. I unwrapped one the first time, my mother's, thick and white with a string. I didn't know what it was. She didn't tell me. I didn't ask. I marvelled at it then stuck it in the waste paper basket under the other things. You never know if a handbag has them in it or not or that a handbag has them also all the time the woman doesn't need them she is a woman because she carries them anyway because they need a handbag and the handbag needs her to be a woman too and the woman needs the handbag so she is a woman to contain the woman things.

Everything is so sticky. I'm meant to be a grown-up now. I'm meant to have given up sticky red things.
I'm a grown-up. I can vote now.
I vote red.

Why does it only announce itself through pain? It hammers and everything is a bit burnt and nauseous, the pot that's red on the outside I remember the feel of that pot it is smooth and matte not quite like velvet the texture of it makes me feel sick. Something was burnt on I think. I couldn't get it off.

Those ads on the telly that show it blue not red, they say you can ignore it. You can ignore something only if you know it's there.

Marigolds

What I don't say:
Any of this.

And that light that light that comes in the evening: yellow, with a white centre you can't look at just as it's going behind the hills at the edge of the valley not that they're hills it's that we're in a dip they're a rim really and splayed against it a cloud really dark really blue grey with through it holes with shafts of light that go through it and down that look like boxes, long narrow boxes that reach down to the ground like they had sides like they were 3d.

It's about this time my mother puts on her rubber gloves they're yellow, yellow as the light on the edge of the sunset around the white in the middle, yellow as the haze that hangs in the air as the 3d boxes that stretch all the way from the clouds to the fields and she makes small movements they are circular she scrubs the pans the surfaces sometimes the floor with its hole in the tiles that aren't tiles not really you unroll them like a carpet we have a spare roll under the stairs. She does this all facing away from the sunset because the kitchen is on the other side of the house from the sunset and the kitchen surfaces in any case face away from the windows and are lit by tubes that are stuck underneath the wall cupboards you can see if you peer underneath and she faces away from the sunset until it's all gone and she doesn't have to do it or she doesn't have to do it so thoroughly or she doesn't have to do it then how many sunsets has she missed?

After which she sits in a dark room where people are tested on the television. They have to know all sorts of things and sometimes she can answer, mostly wrong but differently wrong from the people on the television so she looks happy and even as tho she might be right after all. The knowledge is nothing to do with the valley. Nothing of our lives here can be known. Or the knowledge has no use, or maybe no value. He watches them too. It's not her only. When the answers are given he mouths them half a syllable behind. As if he knew them too.

There is such security in the way I hate them. I look up to the corner of the window still lit. There it is, solid.

Sun

Then mum and dad watch the telly until one of them goes to sleep.

All I can see out here are wordless things and also silent out of my window between the sunset the new houses' bones black beyond, among them the long grasses bending gold on top green under then black. There's nothing to say about it.

I play my music quiet. I lie with my head right by the tape recorder so as not to disturb. I lie on the floor I can smell the carpet. It smells like the coat of something live an animal perhaps but its fibres snag my nails because they're not woven they're extruded or whatever. The fibres glisten. You can only see that from close up.

They are nothing natural.

The carpet is always damp. I remember when they took it up. The bottom was clammy rubber. It was peach. The colour peach, not the colour of peaches. Now there are patches in like crop circles the pile laid down where people have trod. You can smell the smell of people along with the rubber if you put your face close. It's almost like skin.

I lie behind curtains looking up at them I can see between the curtain and the lining they are cotton and if you lie under them on the floor right by the wall you can look inside and they're like a cone where you can see the light through until late. Outside my window the sunset until what 9 or even later.

My hand strays on me. Like it's not mine.

They are moss green the curtains they have small flowers. The flowers are white. You can see the sun clearer through the white bits. I go to bed rather than stay downstairs. I have to be a child for only a little while longer.

I arrange my books by colour in the order of the rainbow.

Blue Moon

In the dark now white things, the moths, the bones of something in the hedge showing white.

On the hill opposite a stick (unseen) with red things, lords and ladies, a radio mast. It's so the planes can see it.

On the ring road the houses turned away behind raw fences, bats in the gardens, in quite suburban houses. I have never seen them down by the river.

I can stay here 'til the light fades and never notice. My eyes change with the dark.

Blue moon which is not blue, only whiter, like Persil.
(That's a joke).
'Where did you put your things?'
(I can hear them downstairs.)
'Did you wash the tomatoes before slicing them?'
'On top of yours, ready to go in.'
'In this plastic bag I have put all the things we are going to wear Sunday.'
'Did you wash the tomatoes before slicing them?'
'No it isn't. It's going to stay very mild next week.'
'I've got this egg here. Can I put it in the suitcase? A brown egg.'
'You didn't, did you?'

'A brown egg? It has nothing to do with the suitcase.'
—Noise of rustling—

'Agugh, dammit'
—Noise of rustling—
'At the side of the dresser. To the left'
'There's a mark on these shorts. Do you need them for anything at all?'
'Shorts?'
'I mean trousers'
—rustle!—
Onlyclank
Onlyclank
'Padon?'
Murmer.
'Ush'
'I wedge the door'
'Ulppppadon me'
'Ow-ehew'
Persil washes whiter but its grains are blue.

Radio Midnight

Things I don't know:

I don't know where the river goes.
Because I do not know the river goes nowhere.
In the meantime the estate is not the valley.
The valley is not the estate.
I'm not sure which one is right.
When I go to one I forget the other.
Except in patches where it shows through in the pub by the river in the green by the bus in the new town not so much. Even the trees there have nothing to do with the trees here.

I must sit and listen to what isn't here. To catch it. When I go to the estate I cannot hear nothing again.

Even here and now I hear the ring road in the distance.

And:

That sound on the radio late at night the dial turned to nowhere. Notes play, each equal, long. What is it plays them? A tune played by people who don't understand music. I think it is a Russian tune. It is a code like morse code. A Russian code? It only happens at night.

The last thing to go is the shipping forecast. The last thing before dark noise. Sometimes I stay up late my parents asleep I'm not tired. I listen to all the things that tell me it's late: the late news the late book then the shipping forecast then they play a tune then nothing.

Then the sound.

And across the fields.

Is it a sparkling ocean?

It is a sea of plastic. There is no ocean here.

Its waves move, catch the moon, leap to it, ripple with white noise.
It is alive.

But it is not nature. So my feelings for it are wrong.

It is something about which no stories can be told.

June

Garden

I am a feminist.
I don't like any of the women here.

Smell is made of molecules.

At the cattery, chicken wire fronts the cages.

The molecules of cat shit hang in the air. Some must stick to the inside of my nose. The cats all eat meat. Their shit is sticky. The gravel in the cat trays sticks to it. I switch on my walkman. It is the tape I made from the radio.

I have a plastic scoop. I unlock each cage and take a scoop of gravel around the shit. I put this into a sack. I listen to *Robert De Niro's Waiting* by Bananarama.

I am a feminist.
I am reading a book about sex. It is by a man.
I have finished my exams. I have lots of spare time.

I go under the underpass.

I pass

S

E

X

Nobody knows I am reading the book.
I can hear the cars above me.

I have nothing much to do 'til October.

Home: my mother under the sycamore on the sun lounger in the garden oils her body, her skin nylon as her swimming costume. I know its nude lining very well, the loose skin of a soft doll. Her belly is round even when she lies flat, not grotesquely but obscenely. It is not fat this spare flesh: she has it from me. How can she bear to show it? If you get close enough you see a network of fine white lines. I test 'mother' on the woman in front of me, against the word I've read in books. This is difficult because the mothers in books are so entirely busy with their function.

You can 'have' sex but you can't keep it.
There is nowhere to keep it in your body.
Sex is what you can't tell if anyone has.
They won't necessarily lie to you.
They just won't say anything.

That smell, the earth and squashed grass combined that is like the innermost of sweat like outdoor sweat on the palms rubbed together, quite fresh and like nature with the dirtiness of bodies, quite different from the dirtiness of the earth that is not really at all dirty because it does not have one body rubbing against itself or against other bodies but is lots of different things each blade different. Only human sweat binds its own smells together reminding us we are not nature oh no not really.

Rosemary's body smells quite different to her sister's which is sharp sour a bit masculine. Rosemary is lime playdoh dirt should I notice this?

My mother further off like chip oil my father sometimes a bit like cat shit especially in the mornings that round blunt fuzzy smell like shit yes but not quite. No sister brother don't know what someone else my age... Rosemary's sister's sharp crease at her thigh brown and worms of sweat I can see the bulge where she wears the thick pad for her cystitis not meant to notice that either nor does she, like we ignore it when we bleed, not speak, no smell, no stain but I can detect my own rusty tinge its molecules in the air nevertheless.

I think Rosemary has done it.
But I cannot ask her about it.

A tree: an explosion happening very slowly.

Float

There is another painting. It is on my teacher's wall in her school office.

When we are in the stream me and Rosemary we do not swim, we pretend. It is too shallow. We lie in it the cold covering our backs and our sides sometimes letting the water snake its way around our fronts between our legs over our waists where they dip. If we push our hair out behind us it flows to show the stream's still flowing. We are just like the painting.

She is a teacher of English Literature. On her office wall which is the office wall of the English Department is a girl lying in a stream. It is pasted onto board and varnished, bright. You can see all the small leaves as if you could focus everywhere at once. The girl looks neither happy nor unhappy. She looks incapable of her own distress. She looks up into air. Her mouth is open, catching flies.

We do not think what we look like.

But in the picture is one of the streams that is not ours. It is greener, lusher. There are willows athwart the bank. Athwart. It is in England. Or it is in English Literature. We are not in England. I mean here in the valley. Or we are not in English Literature. In England, or in Literature at least, there are punts water meadows cows meadows a-chewing a-mooing to pass the time away a sleek sinuous full-bodied animal chasing and chuckling gripping things with a gurgle and leaving them with all the birds of oxfordshire and gloucestershire I'd rather reign with Edmund there than be all England's queen what spires what farms are those? Here in not-England the water's dark you can't see beyond the bank if there's barbed wire wheat stubble a metal bridge crumbled concrete. In the painting there are plants I recognise: dog rose loosestrife that liberal shepherds call a grosser name dock unless I'm seeing them wrong but in the painting they are all discrete and not mixed as they are by the stream where we can't see what is rooted where.

I cannot swim.

We are reading English Literature to tell us what England is.
I have never lived in England.
I have lived here all my life.

Rosemary can swim.

It might be a shallow stream like ours her back—the girl's—might be catching against the mud the gravel the long weeds otherwise how would she float like that?

But Rosemary lies on her back and floats under the bridge.
And so do I.

Fear

Things I don't talk about:

My mother keeps things in she doesn't talk about. They are things we don't eat, tins: spam, oxtail soup. She keeps in bags of lentils and chickpeas: we don't eat those either. They are in case.

The four most harmful radionuclides spread by the disaster were iodine-131, caesium-134, caesium-137 and strontium-90 with half-lives of 8.02 days, 2.07 years, 30.2 years and 28.8 years respectively.

(It's hard to think about everything looking the same after the grass green and the meat red and the sun still in the same place like a picture we don't know and we can't know. It happened two years ago there but we didn't know, not 'til the spring after.)

Caesium tends to accumulate in vital organs such as the heart, while strontium accumulates in bones.

(About fifty years old when it reduces even once.)

One villager says: 'We had a year once when almost every day there was a funeral. We must have buried about fifty people that year. Is it related? Who knows.'

(The poppies if you pick them the petals all fall off more or less straight away even if you put them right into water.)

Throughout the European continent, in nations where abortion is legal, many requests for induced abortions, of otherwise normal pregnancies, were obtained out of fears of effects, including an excess number of abortions in Denmark in the months following the accident.

(I still pick them.)

Officials estimate the area cannot be safe for human life again for another 20,000 years.

To be unable to think of it but to think it anyway. But not to talk about it. Is that love?

Swim

My mother says she can teach me to swim. It goes like this she says and throws one arm over the other when we are very far from water.

My mother does not like to swim. She said, *but I can teach you without going in.*

I can teach you to dance, says my mother. Ballroom. Latin. I used to. Every Friday.

My mother imitates a pirouette which I know is nothing more than an imitation of a pirouette with its suggestion of elegance and expertise all the same carried out in earnest but for what purpose? Why for attraction of course, what else is dancing for? Real dancing is not about attraction but skill. To aim at attraction is to miss. She learnt not how to pirouette, but to pretend to.

What she is teaching is obvious pretence.
What she is teaching is that pretence must be obvious.
To remain incomplete I must show some incapability.
To show incompletion means I show I that I might be completed.
She does not teach me who I should show this to.

She never says any of these things to me aloud.

I pirouette in turn very poised showing no damage but some incapability.

Smile!

Having learned to show enjoyment I am pretending also to enjoy it.

Miss

The grass is bitter. It is dark and strong. Pick a blade, when you press it, it's wet.

Twice a week I mop the cages.

I am sitting waiting for Rosemary and her sister on the steps of the mobile library. I am waiting for Rosemary's sister to finish her tennis lesson. The tennis courts are by the church.

I listen to Queen. I put the tape on before I go in there. I listen to We Are The Champions. I have on plastic gloves not rubber gloves but disposable plastic gloves. They are too big for me. They rustle. I have a mop and the scooper and the bag for cat shit and the bucket with water and disinfectant I get the water from the tap on the outside of the cattery I get the disinfectant from the cupboard by the food bin I lock the door and let the cats from one cage out into the corridor between the cages while I clean the cage they have just vacated. First I remove the bed then I clean out the entire gravel in the trays, not just the shit, tipping it all into the sack, then I use the scoop to scrape any remaining shit off the trays. If the trays are really dirty I stack them up. There is a pile of clean trays by the side of the door I put them there earlier. They are from vacant cages I lean through the door to the outside and sweep anything up with a dustpan and brush I mop the floor inside the cage I fill the clean tray with new litter. By this time the cage is dry. I put the bed back in I get the cat or cats and put them in I lock the door and start on the next cage.

What grows on the tennis courts is clover & daisies. You can make the daisies into chains, and you can pluck out the petals of the clover and suck their bases. These taste weakly of sugar.

When I do this I have been told to worry about dog piss.

Rosemary arrives she has some chocolates.

When a cat scratches you the lines of blood are very thin. After a few hours they itch. After a day you can pull off long thin strings of skin from the scar.

When Rosemary's sister's finished we say let's go to the stream and we all cycle different ways and see who gets there first. I go on the cycle path by the ring road, turning right at

S

E

X

going under the underpass, through the plantation by the executive estate, past my house and up to the ridge by the cattery then down into the valley Rosemary goes straight through the village and up the hill to the ridge then down Rosemary's sister is a fast cyclist she goes right through the village and over the stream in the village by the pub then round the road on the other side of the stream that goes along the ridge on the other side of the valley. We are meeting at the bridge in the middle.

When I've finished with the cages and they're all locked with the cats back inside I take the sacks of gravel and cat shit and put them in the cinder-proof bin at the end of the drive and from there I can see the bridge and the stream then I go back and scrape the dirty trays under the tap in the trough outside the cattery, and I—

When I get to the bridge Rosemary is there but not her sister. We go under the bridge. We stay there for a long time.

—I have listened to both sides of all three of my tapes. I have been on my own all this time. I am satisfied.

We wait and Rosemary's sister doesn't come but we're not at all alarmed about this, and when I begin to get alarmed it's quite an artificial kind of alarm at first and it seems this way for Rosemary too.

(Around Rosemary and her sister I identify eager and dread.)

Outside the cattery I can smell cat shit in the air. I hope I don't smell of cat shit and that it's only that the molecules are now on the inside of my nose.

I thought the stems of the chocolate cherries Rosemary brought were real but when I examined them closely, each was identical, plastic.

I don't know if you can get blood poisoning from cat scars. There is nowhere I can look this up.

Things we don't talk about:
1. That Rosemary's sister is not here.
2. Whether she passed while we were under the bridge.
3. If we should have waited for her.
4. That we do not talk about this.
5. Whether we feel any kind of alarm.

Alarm

Then the noise filling everything all the molecules in all the air that bounces off one side of the valley then the other meeting itself halfway the noise of something happening.

It is both the inside and the outside of my head. It is the loudest sound I have ever heard.

(We're lying at the bridge, me and Rosemary. We lie flat. Every molecule in our bodies is sound. We wait for the noise to pass through them.)

It is a warning warning.

Things I don't talk about:

Ransoms. Vetch curling. Rape. Solomon's seal.

Residents left baffled by a loud siren on Sunday can rest easy that it was not warning of a 'nuclear attack', but caused by a chlorine alarm test. Readers contacted the council after hearing a wailing noise that started at about 3.20pm and sounded like an air raid siren.

Woodruff.
The occasional dead man's finger.

The council said the siren is based at its Green Farm sewage works and is meant to warn residents of a chlorine spill. The new siren is being tested each

Sunday at noon beginning next week, according to Mike Whitham of the County Emergency Management Agency. This particular siren is used only in case of a hazardous materials leak, not for any other type of emergency.

Lords and ladies.
(Dicklike. Possibly.)
Saxifrage.

If the siren is activated, those who hear it should go inside, shut all windows and doors, and turn off air intake systems such as heating and cooling systems. Cracks in windows and doors should be sealed with duct tape if possible. The public should then tune to local radio for further instruction and information.

Goldenrod.
Dog violet.

The new siren was funded by the county council in response to community concerns after discussions with the emergency department, which handles hazardous material incidents. The Power, Water and Sewerage System and River Electric Department cooperated to install the siren.

Purple loosestrife.
Green hawthorn berries slightly coloured now. Red.

The intent is for the siren to remain on as long as danger is present, although the absence of the siren should not be taken as an 'all clear,' since the siren is capable of failure. Roving police car loudspeakers, as well as local radio, give the official 'all clear' signal.

The weather on bank holidays is very often overcast.
Can loosestrife be replaced with anxious?
Can oats be replaced with fury?
Can saxifrage be replaced with violent?

Nothing happened.
Only fear not converted into action.
The noise stops: the fear stays with us.
Things I don't talk about:
We do not stop being afraid.

Plantation

You can walk through the plantation tho it belongs to someone. Plantations always do.

There are traps somewhere. But there are paths.

1. Barbed wire.

2. A feeling of being watched.

It is quiet. However

in someone else's eyes I can always go wrong.

Things I don't talk about:

When everyone else is out, sometimes, milk and sherry in a special glass. Not much. Top of the milk, if I can with the crusty bits around the top where the cream rises and you scrape your finger round and it tastes a bit off. It's called a cocktail. I've seen them drink it on the telly. You use just a bit from everything so no one sees: the sherry, the bells, the martini, with the milk, even all together if you like. My dad comes back from work and every night he changes his work clothes then he has a bells. Every night. After that it's lager.

The garlic in the woods smells wrong so I ignore it. Something culinary about it but not quite. It smells like a smell people don't like so better to not think about it, especially if not alone. Sometimes I ignore it even to myself.

Sometimes I ignore that I also enjoy it.

Milk spilt on the kitchen lino made to look like tiles.

A tear in the tiles. The milk goes in.

No.

That's a joke isn't it. They don't look like tiles any more. You can see the ridge between two strips where it wasn't glued down properly. That'll be the damp.

During the cocktail the house is funny: the kitchen tops that look like wood; the sides of the tops where you can see the crunched-up wood they're made from, the kitchen cupboards that look like wood the same.

A joke. The countryside here is wrong always. I am disappointed.

It should be you know rolling hills whatever water meadows bullrushes little boats people in white, green.

We hear woodpeckers we think but don't see them.

By now the wheat is maximum gold.

Factory

I walk through the plantation so the man can show me his egg factory. I have to carry a message for my mother. I can't remember what.

The egg factory is a barn. It is dark with a few lights. He left me there but it is ok. He had to do something I don't know what. I was alarmed but it was ok.

Oh yes, I am there to buy eggs. For the party. For boiled eggs. And cakes.

In the dark the chickens cover all the floor of the barn.

They run round and round all together. They run towards each other. They avoid each other. Then they meet the next chicken.

They do not ever go outside the barn.

The lights are on. They hang from the ceiling. It is still dark.

Hybrid hens that are selectively bred to lay hundreds of eggs are the usual producers of soft / shell-less eggs. It is not uncommon for commercial 'brown hens' to lay 320 or more in a year and

I know this is not the worst kind of egg factory.
So I force myself to feel it.

the normal 'shelling process' usually taking around 24 hours can be followed in some heavy layers by a shell-less egg produced in less than 12 hours.

By the corner of the chicken factory the road goes uphill through the plantation by the executive estate. (There is a house at the top of the hill. A boy I know lives there.)

The plantation is fir trees, no grass under them. The ground under the trees is covered with brown needles. It is soft and springy. In the plantation nothing changes, winter or summer, not even the noise. There is no noise. That is why I am frightened.

That is why I am frightened when there is someone else on the road.

(He is the boy with the swimming pool in his garden.)

The eggs from battery chickens come in grey cardboard. These eggs from the chickens in the egg factory that is not the worst come in grey cardboard. You can't tell the difference.

(Where I swam once with Rosemary.)

Round here you still buy things direct from the farmer sometimes. Eggs I mean. That's what my mother wanted. I remember. She wanted the cheap eggs that have soft shells. I pay, I take the eggs.

(Why did he show me?)

The cheap eggs are soft and wrinkly like skin. The same colour too. If you press into them your finger goes in but the shell does not break. Sometimes it's only a few in the tray, sometimes a dozen. The farmer sells those trays cheap.

If you don't mind the skin he says there's nothing wrong with them.

Feet

I take my shoes off to walk to the river. The road is tarmac, hot, soft. Outside the cattery there is white gravel, large chips of stone. This is harder, but my feet are getting tougher.

The red post office van drives across the other ridge. I see it every day.

On the bridge there is room for only one car to go over at a time.

On the road down to the bridge there is a bit more room but not much.

After it's happened when there aren't cars any more I don't know what— maybe horses. There are people here with horses in the village. I don't know them but I see the horses pass the end of the garden sometimes and I see marks left in the mud when I haven't seen the horses pass.

The edges of my feet are white.

Now there are cars but not so many down the valley. Some of them are male some of them are female. We lie on the bridge Rosemary and me and look at the cars from ground level, at the workings underneath as they get near. The male ones have pipes, the female, two hard bumps together. If you lie on the bridge that's the level you see them from: male, male, female, male.

Curious about that engineering, never seen except the outlines. Once a boy. I think I saw. That boy. That is, peeking out of his swim shorts. I don't think he knew I could see. How could he not notice? But, having never seen it in the flesh, I wondered, could I have got it wrong?

(Cars: I am thinking *male, female, male*. I don't know if Rosemary is thinking that too.)

I swam in his pool with Rosemary. We only swam there once.

I am not white, that white anyway. The road is not white. It's grey. The powder that comes between me and the road where we meet is white. Is that off me or the road? My heels have white tracks in like dry mud. The rest of my heels is dark red. Neither is the colour of flesh. My heels look like something in nature.

Do men not know where they are?

Where does all the powder come from, that's between me and everything else in the world?

I don't know how much ground I'd have to cover to leave here.
I can walk, I can cycle.
I cannot drive.
Drivers leave quickly, cyclists less so, walkers slowly.
Walking, it's wrong not to notice each house, each tree.
It's wrong not to notice each blade of grass.

I can hear the noise of the trees. It fills all the space inside my ears.
I must count off every leaf between here and the cattery.

Pool

Rosemary's father is an entrepreneur.

Going with Rosemary her sister her father to the boy's house by the plantation which is also his client's house who is the boy's father. The pool in the garden shaped like a kidney inside it painted blue like nothing in nature Rosemary's father says why don't you get in he says while we talk?

Well that's what we brought our costumes for.
We don't use costumes down at the bridge only shorts or if you have something else on take them off and mostly underwear mostly cotton mostly half covered with something a top or something and then darker where there are splashes transparent even sometimes when we fall in.

We dare each other.

The water in the swimming pool's not heated it's cold, cold as the stream but the feel is not the same.
The water does not move on top of it are leaves lying. By the side of the pool the pool net and Rosemary's sister her legs bent up under her as usual so we don't see them.
She hugs her knees.
The hedge is solid with firs, twenty feet high.
Rosemary's father goes to talk to his client who is the boy's father. The patio door I'd say creaks open but that would be wrong no I don't know how to describe that noise I know what makes it the fluffy stuff on the bottom of the glass the track it almost squeaks but not quite.

It does not seem to be straight on its tracks.
The pane could fall out any time.

Rosemary in her swimming costume. The boy also here, not talking, sent out by his father. Us not talking. Why should he? What would we say to him?

I look at the firs, their tops only waving. The wind doesn't get to them. Nothing gets through them. They make us dark.

The sun makes us dark.

I can't see inside the house it's dark. One of the patio doors, slid behind the other, reflects white, the opening straight to black. No not black there is no black in nature. I walk round the pool to follow Rosemary to the jumping end her sister frozen mid-air as I turn, too close to the opening on purpose and turn my head just at the right time. Inside a dark carpet: brown, perhaps, too little furniture a glass dining table Rosemary's father sitting talking to a man I cannot see.

(We know we are being watched.)

There is an inside to the firs somewhere if you focus on it there is a black part blacker than any other. This is also true of the house.

(We are also watching. But we do not know who sees that.)

I stand in the shallow end of the boy's swimming pool and wheel my arms like my mother says.

The stream in the valley is shallow; my feet always on the ground.

Nothing happened.

I am afraid to swim in deep water.

Lace

Cars seldom came over the bridge by the stream. When we see one coming we hide underneath in the bridge up to our waists our clothes wet on us like bodies like other bodies. That cool damp smell. The car passes rumbles over us and our laughs rumble inside us like sex perhaps. Like sex we clutch ourselves in several places.

Things I don't talk about:

The men are working in the field next door. They are mixing concrete. The house is empty. I rinse the cream ring from the sherry glass and go upstairs. I don't know why I do this, no I know. I look through my mother's things I pick things up. I put them down again, carefully, in their dust marks all that stuff the nail varnish the rings the hair dye the falsies. In my father's drawer those things I know what they are but don't know quite, rubber in foil packets wet as inside bodies something live. I follow a set path but pretend I am quite casual. In my mother's drawer her push-up bra. I put it on. Her lace suspender belt her thong. I put them on. White lace not white quite still queen anne's lace. I go to the window. I hang back. They do not see me, the men outside. My nipples push over the top. I let them.

I want them to see me.
I don't want.

The stream. The fish go through my hands. I catch them alive. I squeeze (I don't squeeze). I put them in the jar. They live. But then we let them go.

I am not doing it again. I start not doing it tomorrow. Tomorrow I don't do it as much. I am counting how many times. No times is ideal but a few times is not bad. When I have done it enough. (And I have done it enough (I do it one more time to make sure).)

The sound of a shot across the field a scarecrow mechanism. It is not a real shot, it is no reason to be alarmed.

I take off her my clothes and I am not a woman. The relief! The woman was too tight dug into my ribs her pads pushed my breast in her lace was scratchy. I can put her off now.

Our legs are wet numb rubber. Half of our bodies in a different element, Rosemary and me.

The men are gone anyhow and now children are in the field I don't know how they got in. They sound like a swimming pool. Their voices don't come from the same place as their bodies: they bounce off the walls of unfinished brick. I don't see them. They're screaming, the kind of screams that must be play, but not how adults like children to play which is quiet and contained, and going along expected lines so not really play not at all. They're screaming I don't know what: argument excitement violence pleasure joy. It's frightening. It's frightening to hear something so uncontrolled. It's also nice.

(I keep that last bit secret from myself.)

Ants

On the concrete bridge there are ants. The ants stay mostly by the lip where the bridge meets the road in a tiny step measuring a millimetre or two. Maybe there is some shade there.

There are things it is too hard to think about. They are not happening here in the valley.

Rosemary bends down over her left leg. She uses her nails to push together a darker spot. She does this slowly. A hair coils out of the spot, an inch or so long, perfect.

Some ants go in one direction by the concrete lip and some in the other. I won't call them a line of ants because there aren't that many of them, and they are in single file, but there are generally two of them quite close together going in one direction, and two going in the other. When the ants going in one direction meet the ants going in the other, they stop before they go round them. They don't seem to have any expectation of meeting.

I mean things like starving and maiming and killing and people who are starved and maimed and killed. They are not round here but their shadow still falls on us. We are told only to think about them when we're told to. When I think of them something turns my thought away quickly. If we think about them we have to think beyond the valley.

I lie flat along the concrete, can feel the ridge just under my breasts. I lie so my breasts hang over the edge. If I don't it is uncomfortable. I can lie like this for a while before the concrete ridge starts biting in. That's gravity pushing me into the ground.

Everyone stayed in and watched the telly when they played live, the song about the people dying, but I was out somewhere in the valley. I didn't see it. I didn't want to see it. There's wrong with it. I can't work out what. I don't want to be involved. I was out somewhere, maybe down the valley. I was trying not to think about it because it was too complicated. I knew there was something bad about not staying in to watch the telly of the performance of the song about the people dying, or I felt wrong about it but there also seemed something wrong about the song too. Or about sitting in and watching the telly and not giving any money. Or even buying the record and enjoying the song as many times as you like and thinking about the people dying at the same time at that proper time and place there is still something I don't like about it and I still can't work it out.

Sometimes we put things in the way of the ants, like twigs and blades of grass, and if they don't go under, they always go round. Sometimes we put things right to the edge of the bridge but they still go round, just crawling along the side.

I still hear it a lot the song because especially people play it at parties, so that parties are now always also about those other people that we can't imagine doing anything except dying. We have so many other things to do but it looks like dying is the only thing they do because it's all we are told they do and it becomes even harder to think about them because every time we think they are still dying so that everything we do when we play the record is part of their dying especially any time we try to do the opposite of dying like having parties. When the song is repeated we are thinking about them but we are not doing any more than that. We are told to have fun at parties. We are told we should have fun, and we should have parties to have fun at. We are told not to have fun when we think about people dying. When the song is played at parties all we can do is think and not do anything about the people dying. We cannot do anything unless we leave the parties. We don't leave. That's why we smash things after parties. In defiance of our lives.

Rosemary's dad bought her the record about people dying. She put it on for us. She laughed at it.

I didn't like that not the song not laughing at the song not that the song existing meant that it could be laughed at and along with that the people dying could be laughed at. And I did not like Rosemary for a moment for a moment only.

But at the same time I admired her.

The print of concrete on the insides of my arms.

Rosemary said, It's not a big deal.

She started tracing a pattern with a straw over her leg and forgot about it.

The grasses bend back, their reverse-sides white.

There are no people dying here in the valley, not like that anyway. There are poor people maybe the ones living in the tower blocks in the centre but most of us live on the estate and in the village and between the village and the estate and on the executive estate or in the old town. None of us are dying. Not all the time anyway. None of us are spending all our lives dying. We don't have lives like that. We can't think about people dying not when we think about our lives.

The fields stroked all the wrong way.

Gable

Things I don't talk about:

It

You can't get it any other way except books or at least I can't there must be people who buy those magazines in the newsagent. I flick my eyes upward and they are hanging over me lots of them a whole shelf. By people I mean men. I mean men must buy them and they're all about women but if they have stuff about it in that means they must have stuff about men too. I can't reach up and take one down it's not what girls do I have to pretend I'm not interested.

I can't even look.

The boy who lives up the road well it's more like a mile away in the big house with the swimming pool. He's my age and when we are all about to die I don't know how there are so many ways I am planning to go over and ask him to do it to me.

In the meantime I know you can find stuff about it in books.

I read Colette. She is French.
I bring the book home from the library. My dad says:
Isn't that... adult?
I don't know so I don't answer. I don't see anything adult in the book by

Colette if adult means stuff about it. Bodies I mean. Then I think of a bit where a man breaks a glass. He falls over. He sees the woman looking down at him and there seems something adult about this because I don't understand it quite. It was something powerful, but I don't quite know why but I knew that not quite knowing must be part of its adultness. I put the book down. Unable to expect what I might encounter, I could not pick it up again.

My dad has not read Colette. On his shelves, thrillers, detective stories. They have stuff about it in them, bodies I mean. That's what I look for along his shelves. That must be adult because it's what adults do. But not the same as Colette.

There are so many things I don't know, how should I know which things I shouldn't see?

I am alarmed by the books even the ones here on the shelves the books that are my dad's about men and their bodies men doing things leaping from one thing to something else or doing it and maybe they're spies or explorers but some of them are other things there are also more serious books I can tell by their covers and they are also by men. I am frightened to read books about men, by men. I don't know what those books can do to me. I know they can do something.

I walk past the boy's house. The house is his skin altho
I don't know if he's even in.

To touch these books is like touching a man's body.

The house is big and red and faces in several directions. Most houses face back and front sometimes a tiny window on the side for a bathroom if they're not terraced. This house has small pointy roofs that are called gables at different angles. I don't know what the rooms inside must be like some of them overhanging the first storey the windows all at different levels. I thought at first it must be an old house but no there's a plaque on the front it says 1905 in crinkly writing like it wants to be older. There are beams but I thought they were real not like the ones you see on some of the houses on the estate where people have put them on just stuck them to the front like it makes their house look older or to show they'd like their houses to look older because they don't. But this house has beams and they're not painted black they're just pale grey wood-colour like they've been there for a long time in all weathers without varnish and they're inside each gable and on top of each gable red tiles. Because the house faces in several directions at once you can't be sure which is the front door maybe there isn't such a thing though I don't know where they know to put the post through. You can tell the house is some sort of old nevertheless as all the plumbing pipes are on the outside like they had to stick them on after. And round this house there's gravel not white like on some of the houses in the estate but grey like the beams. And after that lawn and on all sides the tall fir trees of the plantation that mean the lawn gets bare and short underneath not the same grass as ours this grass is green and short with no clover and under the trees it is straw-coloured with moss. I know that kind of grass have sat on it. The short hairs prick your shaved legs like stubble and when you get up you have red dots I generally swing my legs under me right to left my right heel wedged into my — using any of the words for it sounds wrong as there's not a word for it not one that can make it sound nice. Wedged into. It. Hot around my heel.

I am not those words not any of them.

So I just won't mention it.

Sometimes I walk past his house to see if he's still there.

I am alarmed by my dad's books but there aren't any other sort of books here. There are no books by Colette not here and not in school either. Reading in class was different even books about it because the books are given to us and we read them in daylight and sometimes aloud and also we read them because we had to and because no one read them by choice except if wanting to show they'd chosen to read a clever thing. I don't know where in the valley I can both find a book by Colette and read it on my own.

I don't know him really I just know him to look at. He comes out of his house dressed in that black blazer with the badge on the pocket like all the rest of those boys and black trousers and white shirts like a boy wearing a suit which is strange until you see him meet up at the bus stop with the other boys wearing suits and there are far more of them than girls like me not wearing a suit because in my school you didn't have to but it's a school bus that takes people into the Old Town from the village. Apart from that he has curly hair and lips too big for his face apart from that I can't think what his body is like under that suit except that I think it is very white like roots.

I think of him because he is my age.
He is not the worst boy I have seen.
And those are the reasons I would ask him.

Gran

There have been no men on the building site for a week now.

Something happened. Gran fell down. Mum's mum I mean. Mother. Mother's mother. Nobody found her. She fell down in the bathroom. A neighbour found her. She was talking about policemen. She is in the hospital. The postman found her. He looked through the letterbox. She thought she was being arrested. We sit in the car until it is time to visit. Her toes are yellow. She cannot cut her toenails. We do not cut her toenails. When we left she cried, not out loud, but tears came out of her eyes.

All the earth in around the new houses was mud. Now it is cracked.

The hospital is on the ring road and it smells of car park, all of it. It is car park colour, all of it.
Petrol and plastic.

There is still an alarm in the air in the valley. It hangs, not making a noise. It is there nonetheless.

Gran says the women in the next beds take the toilet rolls there are never any in the bathroom.

Even the cellar is dry. Around the walls a green stripe shows water level.

Here is the bottle of Love Musc. It fits in my palm. It is round and flat and
cool. I have brought it here for something. For something to hold on to.
It smells just like the car park.

Nothing hangs together.

The nurse says in any case she can't get up to go to the toilet.
She is my mother's mother. My mother should have cut her toenails.
The nurse says she is telling stories.

If I were a mother gran would be a mother's mother's mother.

I could be a mother.
Rosemary could be a mother.

Rosemary does not tell me about doing it.
I do not ask her.

There are no stories about people like us.

See two women. Always, 'I want to be *that* one'. Without even thinking.
See me and Rosemary. I would not want to be me.

Hoverflies are wrong. They are a deception. Wasps are bad but they are not
wrong. Bees can sting but they are still good. And you don't see them often. Other
insects: common blue, soldier beetle, caddisfly.
Does it matter I know these names?

I don't see myself in any of this.

Meadowsweet is fluffy.
Old man's beard is fluffy. The last not flowered yet.
The cow parsley is gone.
Vetch. Yarrow. Milkwort, milfoil, st john's wort, scullcap, trefoil.

I am avoiding photographs right now.
But I can feel how it is to look at things.

Look closely at the leaves and they have holes in them. Something has eaten
them, what began in spring no longer perfect.

I think about 'mother' and 'dead' so I feel a tug of affection. I think
it is affection. I give it the name just so I can feel this.

Honeysuckle it's called woodbine in Shakespeare. Woodbine is old-fashioned
cigarettes. I don't know why.
Bramble blossom.
And cherries squashed by the roadside, red, too bitter.

What is it like to be one of those women (any women really). I can
see them but I can't feel it.
(What is it like to be Rosemary?)

Plums

...And now I'm waiting waiting for the bus. I am carrying a bag of plums in my lap and the grass tickles under my legs. I feel, what? Fruitful? I don't really know what that means.

Waiting waiting for the bus. There is nobody else here. The wind is sinister because unseasonal at least according to the season in books. Summer is sunny. This is England but it is not. The bag is paper some juice from the plums is seeping through. Also from the juice from stones of the ones I have eaten.

I am a feminist.
I am not like the other girls.
My body is a girl but I am not.
My body does not look like how a girl should look.
This is why I am reading a book by a man.

The grass is the colour of school grass, which is not the colour of grass in books but is aggressive, particularly strong and blue. The blades of school grass are almost white underneath. They are tough and too thick to whistle with. They are the same all the year. They are always cold.

Chaucer said:
Shakespeare said:

Sometimes I can't see anything but their backs, their print blouses, their hair done up quaintly. But sometimes I catch a whiff of it, that they're like us, those girls in books. Not costumes but their bodies just like ours, everything else surface, especially the words...

More facts:
Bismarck said:
Tolstoy said:

But there were never any stories about the valley. No words have been used here.

Fruitful: the same feeling as the blood in church.

For something to be real it must be said. Stories are the only real things. There are no old things in the valley except nature and nature's never old. In the Old Town there's a shop with stuff, old stuff like jugs for cider and things for hitting rugs to get the dust out, and horse brasses. Some of them only look old. If you buy them you can make where you are look old, you can make where you are look real.

Sitting by the stop waiting I can feel the long and blue grass on my thighs and I feel capable of carrying—what?

Party

I am at a party. My mother has taken me with her. We are in somebody's front room. We are in the estate. The windows are horizontal rectangles.

Windows should be long. I mean upright.

It is all women. No, there are some old men. They don't count. It is the middle of the day. It is a party for a baby. There are some old women and some women with babies. There are some pregnant women. There are some young girls and other children so young you don't know if they're girls or boys. There is no one my age. All the chairs are set round the walls, so are the garden chairs. They are set against the walls in a square so the most chairs possible can get in. In the other room is only a table with a paper tablecloth. The women bring containers covered in cling film. Each uncovered exhales. The smell released makes me taste it whether I like it or not. The food breathes while I hold my breath. Even so I know that there are things, above all, that breathe cheese. They smell of cheese but taste only sour. I take the sugary things with no smell, the biscuits with pastel foam on top spiked with coconut, those sponge lozenges with a crust. I don't know what they're called.

There are other things I remember yes those whorls of pastry with jam in and cream that is whiter than paper and a network of holes between the holes something sticky that fills up the space. Also small sausages so smooth you could swallow them like pills their insides moussey.

The others eat this stuff but they still look like people.

I never could work that one out.

The cardboard plates bend under the food. You can have two kinds of cake or more and biscuits. There are also crisps pieces of celery pieces of raw carrot.

I cannot find the biscuits I like, so I eat five biscuits I don't like to make up.

I have heels on and a brooch. I dyed the heels red to go with my red lace gloves. *I slipped the brooch into my sleeve. I put it in my hand and turned the display rack. I picked up some earrings in the same hand and slid the brooch into my palm. I slipped the brooch from my palm into my sleeve. I picked up several more pairs of earrings and looked at them before I left.*

No one looks so bad as when they're eating. They take large bites of the cake and pass them from cheek to cheek. My grandfather's mouth puckered like an arse. They don't know what they look like.

You can see the bridge from the cattery. You bike from the kennels taking the road across the ridge then turn right down to the river.

Then there is tea which comes straight after lunch. There is a plate of biscuits with pink middles.

I am passed the baby. It is wet and sour.

I stir my toe in the carpet.

Rosemary's sister is 'athletic'. I don't know what Rosemary is. Rosemary is hot breath.

I can feel the double nylon across my toes.

The baby's back sweats.

I pass the baby back.

I am wearing one of my mother's dresses.

The small fish in the river are bigger now.

We take a jam jar to catch them.

On the verge our bikes are tangled limbs.

I am passed a plate. There is a small sausage, a square of cucumber, half a slice of cake.

The plate is paper it bends. There are crumbs in my lap. I cannot get rid of them.

The cake the sausage have bite marks, the shape of someone's teeth. Then someone is getting up.

There are bags around my feet, on top of my feet. I cannot get up.

I make my feet smaller.

My elbow is against the next woman's. I don't know her. She is talking to someone else.

I press my legs together. Sweat starts between my skin and polyester.

The women each with their secret which is what their bodies look like underneath especially after the baby. The secret is you can't tell under the dress that has wide bits here and gathers and drapes and sometimes corset bits or wide elastic belts and their secret bodies are bundled up and partitioned and stretched and pushed up and smoothed down but you know there's this bit in the middle that has no real form except it keeps changing and there's something frightening about that about the women and the frightening thing is no one's allowed to mention it but you know it's going to happen but you neither know exactly how nor what it means.

Someone is talking to each other.

The carpet is thick and damp and set in whorls; outside it is hot.

They pass the plate. The passing takes so long. It's not the plate it's the passing.

They think they have given me what I want.

No thank you: I cannot take what people give me.

I put my paper plate under the chair. I think of someone standing on it, maybe me. I think of the cake trodden into the carpet. I cannot tell if I enjoy this thought or if it causes me panic.

What am I going towards?

There is no way for us to know what happens outside the valley.

There is radio and TV with play pop music and quiz shows.

There is the news, in which a man puts stories in a straight line from beginning to end before a lady does the weather.

Then there is the local news. That is the town but not the valley.

No one knows what happens here.

Lady fingers (the biscuit), not
Lords & ladies (a plant), or
Dead men's fingers (a plant).
(Also occurring in crab.)
Also

Crab pâté on toast fingers, grey-pink like fingers. Gross.
Long purples. Gross.
I'm not having any of it!

The news is nothing to do with me.
It is nothing to do with the estate, or the valley.
It's not that the news is not relevant.
We are nothing to do with anything.
Nothing has happened here.

I stand up.
I'm getting out of here!

Stop

I am waiting waiting for something to happen. I don't know what it is. I know now is not real time. What's here and now is not worth mentioning. Nothing is happening here except waiting.

I can hear a plane a long way off you don't often hear them there isn't an airport here must be the military.

I am waiting for the bus to the Old Town. Just being in the Old Town is exciting. There is a green there, with something wooden. It looks like a gate with a roof on it. It does not lead into anywhere. It excites me because I don't understand it. In the Old Town there is also the posh kind of supermarket and shops selling women's dresses with hats, and shops where you can sell your own women's dresses if they are the kind of thing that isn't worn out and other women can wear again. And there are estate agents, in every estate agent's window different ways to live, the houses in the windows the smartest. And there are men wearing suits. They're estate agents perhaps. Some of the men have cars. I don't know how old they are. I don't know how old you have to be to be a man or perhaps it's that you have to have a suit. Some of the estate agents look not much older than me. When you look at them carefully they have cuts where shaving has knocked the tops off their spots. But they have suits. Some of the cars are black with long noses. Some of the cars are low and shiny. Some of the suits of the men are black or, not black the word might be 'charcoal'. There are also pubs on the river. I want an estate agent to pick me up in his clean car and take me to a pub on the river. I am not allowed to ask them to do this but I am standing here on the green by the bus stop so one can see me and take me. I know in my heart I am not quite right for them to take me: I have to be older or, not older… different.

When I hear the planes I think what if they don't stop what if the noise just gets louder and louder until

There are trees here too: chestnut trees.
They are better than sycamores.

When I have finished university I see myself working there. At an estate agent. Classy. Like property. I don't know what I do there so I see only parts including only parts of myself wearing a blue suit, perhaps, with a hat like an air hostess. No that's wrong it's just the suit puts me in mind of the hat. The skirt is tight but not too much. Classy. When I am there I have hair that curled halfway down as mine does not. A wave, they call it. It turns out at the middle and under at the ends. I don't know how it does that. My mother, in curlers every morning, every morning early. Heated curlers. For her job. Then leaving. Then coming back. And the next morning the same. I don't know what to do for the estate agent but I know I mostly do what people tell me to. This makes me happy. I think I am carrying a sheaf of papers, taking them from one place to another. I don't know what they are.

I might meet a man there in the estate agent and he might be an estate agent or another kind of man with a clean car and a suit, both dark, and his face tan and blank like I can't see I can see only the stubble and his spots knocked off. We sit outside a pub by the river and it's another summer I'm older or I look it and that bit is like on telly but I can't see any of the other bits. Having formulated only what I wear to work I can't see how I am in order to sit there, though I can see how other women are with long hair and summer dresses drinking something I don't know what. Something in a curved glass. The grass in the pub crushes under my legs which are slick against one another. No they do not I am different then. The blades of grass are cold and blue and thick. They produce moisture. They crush and leave a stain. No they do not I am not stained any more. What should I drink? Cider? I don't know anything else. Beer is too much like a man anyway I don't know the names. Wine is ambitious. Maybe a *white wine spritzer*. (I have heard women sometimes say *a white wine spritzer!*) Then there's the other thing I can't see that we do after. And the other couples in the pub by the river must all do it too though they look much less like bodies than I feel.

The doves' sound is water. It only comes on hot clear days. They start early. There is sun and its partner is the stream. Looking up blinds. So does looking down. It can be a glass of water in the morning. That's the stream too. The water's always there, even when it's not. In the sink, in the shower: that's the stream too. There are patches of shade, the only places you can see in. If you go into the stream on a day like this, it's really entering something different. But it's all around, in the sink, in the glass of water. It's the stuff outside the stream that's less important.

Do I change my clothes between the estate agents' office and the pub by the river? I can't see the gap between the office suit and the dress. Also the hair which, sitting by the river is blonde and, standing in the office is brown. My hair is brown, but not so glossy and dark as the office hair. By the river, different, and also, a straw hat.

The trees thrash. There is always wind in summer here. Sometimes you can't feel it. You just see it in the trees.

Here is my bus. My legs are too cold anyway for sitting on the grass. I am in fact wearing the blue skirt that gathers at the top. I am wearing the white blouse that's bobbled under the arms. I am wearing a white bra that stretches across my breasts slickly and is not white and nor is the blouse not really.

The trees are angry.

It is in fact cold and I am colder. It was hot this morning hot in the cattery under the tin roof where the cat food heated and filled the air with rust. It has become a different day.

Sacha

Rosemary's father lives by the river in the old town. He lives in a warehouse. It is 'reclaimed'.

Rosemary's father has a 4x4. I do not know what an entrepreneur is, not exactly. Men are entrepreneurs. Entrepreneur is one of the many things I don't know about men.

The stream is colder in summer.

We do not drink it, ever.

There are lots of things I don't know about men. I cannot imagine a penis. It goes straight up, they say, like lords and ladies.

I cannot imagine what balls are like.

Rosemary's father lives with his girlfriend. Father is not a word that goes with 'girlfriend'. Rosemary's dad's girlfriend says *call me Sacha*. Sacha is not someone that goes with 'girlfriend'. Who goes with 'girlfriend'? Not me, perhaps Rosemary. Not even her. Sacha is big. She has glasses. She does not dye her hair. Still Rosemary's dad has chosen her and he is an entrepreneur. An entrepreneur with a 4x4 has choice, like an estate agent. Rosemary's stepmother is not like any of the women I know. She wears something with rough textures not a dress because she wears it over a skirt but not a top because it is too long. Rough threads drag from it and this is not wrong but a new kind of right. Rosemary's father cooks vegetables some of which are white and round like breasts and which I do not recognise. Rosemary's father's girlfriend, white and round, lights a long white cigarette on the balcony in the warehouse. The balcony is new. It is made of wood. The wood is rough. The smell of creosote. Inside the flat, just like the outside, the walls are brick.

Rosemary drinks a glass of wine. Her dad says am I allowed. Rosemary hesitates *yes* she says on my behalf. The wine is red but light red almost pink. I've drunk red wine before a bit but not like this.

Rosemary's father and Rosemary's stepmother keep their bread in a tin. An old fashioned one, with a dent in. We keep ours in a thing also made of metal but different, an aircraft hanger whose lid lifts over its plastic base. They keep their glasses on open shelves and they get dust on. They don't have enough of the same kind of glasses, not enough so they all match.

I have never seen any man naked except my dad.
There are 'freestanding bookshelves'.
I have only seen my dad's penis three times, all flaccid.

Rosemary drinks wine. It rains. Rosemary's father's girlfriend goes out on the balcony again. She smokes another cigarette. I cannot call her Sacha.

Close on the hedges, drops. Even here. The very small hawthorn berries. They are here now. It looks like summer but they are here already. They are very pale green.

Rosemary's stepmother lights her cigarette. She asks me about books.

Rosemary's stepmother talks to me like I mean something. But I don't know what.

I don't know if the river in town links up to the stream, or if it's different. Rosemary's father's river's not the stream but it links up somehow. Slow-to-stopping with a green surface gathering round the bridge's red legs. It reminds me.

Across the fields the sound of a shot.

In the communal garden below the warehouse by the river, long grasses between the cobbles.

I can see the balcony across the river. On this side is the medical centre.

I am standing with Rosemary's stepmother and I am smoking a cigarette.

It is 'menthol'. It tastes as strange as the word 'Sacha'.

The rape smells sweet, and also yellow-green.
The inside of my pants are stained yellow, sometimes red.
Sometimes the red turns to blue-grey after the wash.
All this is nothing to do with me.

I do not know anyone else who is divorced, only on the telly.
Telly is a place where people can be divorced. It is different here.
Rosemary's stepmother is a vegetarian.
On Rosemary's stepmother's bookshelves is a book by Colette.

Prion

Things I don't talk about:

It has an incubation period of months to years, during which there are no symptoms, though the pathway of converting the normal brain prion protein (PrP) into the toxic, disease-related PrP^{Sc} form has started. At present, there is virtually no way to detect PrP^{Sc} reliably except by examining post mortem brain tissue using neuropathological and immunohistochemical methods.

You can't tell much from what people look like. People can be pregnant or dying and you still can't tell: in one body there's only so much that appears to be going on.

In humans, autopsy tests are not always done, so those figures, too, are likely to be too low, but probably by a lesser fraction. In the United Kingdom, anyone with possible symptoms must be reported to the Surveillance Unit. The agency relies on other methods, including death certificates and urging physicians to send suspicious cases.

Knots of green: acorn, rose hip, elder. They hurt. Their hurt is there all the time.

The disease may be most easily transmitted to humans by eating food contaminated with the brain, spinal cord or digestive tract of infected carcasses. However, the infectious agent, although most highly concentrated in nervous tissue, can be found in virtually all tissues throughout the body, including blood.

The straw is rolled now; weetabix each with its own track in the snow.

The origin of the disease itself remains unknown. The infectious agent is distinctive for the high temperatures at which it remains viable, over 600 °C (about 1100 °F).

The tracks of the balers. No tracks of men.

This results in protein aggregates, which then form dense plaque fibres leading to the microscopic appearance of 'holes' in the brain, degeneration of physical and mental abilities, and ultimately death.

The fields prickle. They do not bend to the wind.

The British Inquiry dismissed suggestions that changes to processing might have increased the infectious agents.

Dirty stuff in the straw: dock, is it? Everything dying slowly.

It can be in vaccines in medicines in glue on stamps in lollipops and chewing gum and jellies in all good things in all normal things.

This is attributed to the long incubation period for prion diseases, which is typically measured in years or decades. As a result, the full extent of the outbreak is still not known. The Lancet proposed a theory that the most likely initial origin in the United Kingdom was the importation from the Indian Subcontinent. The government of India vehemently responded to the research, calling it 'misleading, highly mischievous; a figment of imagination; absurd,' further adding that India maintained constant surveillance and had not had a single case.

At home flies caught in the corner of the kitchen. They always go to that corner. Three of them. Three different tones.

In the UK, the brain, spinal cord, trigeminal ganglia, intestines, eyes and tonsils are classified as specified risk materials, and must be disposed of appropriately.

Old Girls

Dinner with the grown-ups: Rosemary's father, Rosemary's stepmother, Rosemary's stepmother's student. They are laughing.

I mean the grown-ups are.

I'm afraid I am very sincere.

They are like water meadows.

There are vegetables. The sauce has sesame seeds in. They are toasted. Again it is a thin sauce, not gloomy like sauce is mostly. The vegetables are green but they taste smoky.

'Old girls!'

Says Rosemary's stepmother to her student who is perhaps one year older than me and Rosemary, two.

'Old girls!'

I am afraid I'm not fast enough.

Rosemary's stepmother's student laughs: she is a grown-up; we are not.

'Are gym knickers still compulsory?'

Rosemary laughs.

I do not know what gym knickers are.

'And did you have to wear that *dreadful* beret?'

Rosemary is a grown-up. I am not.

I do not know why berets are funny.

I'm afraid it is wrong for me to be so serious.

Dessert: I do not live in the same world as this custard. Yellow custard solid in the fridge, yes, but not this stuff, pale yellow and thin but less fluid than white sauce on school pudding. Pale yellow, and not thick, and tasting of things I can't identify but they are nice.

Preparing to hear another joke, I listen particularly carefully. Being on the wrong side of funny, I fail to recognise the good bit. Each word becomes something separate, something I think of all the meanings for. I can't keep up. I don't know what it is I must keep up with.

It goes on like this for ages. I am exhausted.

These are the right sort of people. I want to be right. But something here is not right. It must be me.
  There is a point at which I stop trying to find things funny.
  Everyone else finds this funny. I cannot understand this.
  'And did you have to wear that *dreadful* beret?'

I say something at the dinner table: everything points another way quite suddenly as though we were not on solid ground at all but on a ship. I say something and the ship tilts. I didn't know words had such power. My words. It makes a disturbance. People are angry. They don't know why. At first I am upset. This had not been my intention. To take my mind off the tilting I think of the girl in my parents' picture (Is there anyone with her? Is she about to sit down? Is she getting up to leave?), the girl who—I now know—is sitting in a box at the theatre.

And that she was painted by Renoir.

And that Renoir was someone French.

And that is all I know.

Things I don't talk about:

There are tears running down my face I don't know why. They ask me why and I say I don't know.

I don't want to hurt them by telling.

I don't want to hurt myself by telling.

Think:

Saxifrage,

Violent.

Don't think.

Don't think.

Thunder

When dark comes it's like a cloud coming over only it doesn't go away. That's how it is these evenings.

Things I don't talk about:

The flag irises wrapped up in themselves, their heads become rotten green-yellow, carrying seeds, shrivelled skirts around the base.

Don't die of ignorance.

Sometimes you notice a degree darker.
Yellow light that turns the trees green, proper green like a colouring book.

These things still exist whatever we say.
Because the trees know the rain is coming.

'Killer blood,' it said. 'They look just the same as anybody else.'

Everything has joy. The rabbits if you watch them carefully jump on their hind legs. What else are they doing it for? I don't know why, but I know what it is.

Such small things. And still they hit the right scale somewhere. The plant we fished out of the stream. What's the point to such tiny leaves?

'It's terrifying to think this guy was talking to me, or we were drinking in the bar.'

Summer has folded.
Folded in two?
Folded in on itself?

The infection can be passed by intimate contact from one person to another.

It's like thunder.
When there's thunder in the valley you see it after the lightening. The same everywhere I know. You don't shelter under the bridge that's wood and metal. You have no choice but to stand in the rain and the drops are heavy and fat, such discrete things it seems they can't wet you.

(What counts as 'intimate contact'?)

See the clouds speed over the valley, faster at the dip in the middle.
The petals of dog roses fall off when you pick them like the poppies right away. Later there are rose hips. They are not sweet, inside them seeds nothing but seeds all packed in there.
It has to be hot for the poppies to come.

I think I am afraid. I think everyone here is afraid. We stay here only with each other, not letting anyone in, not going outside the valley. But these things we are told have no borders.

End of June. The dark comes in slight wetness in the air. It is still summer.

(Can we have a life out here?)

Do nothing...
Do nothing...
Do nothing...

Sometimes something comes to the surface. You don't see it. You see the ring it has made. You hear the noise after.

Think nothing. Then you won't be able to do it.

Night Walk

Something white down by the river, I thought an old duvet, like the tramps leave sometimes. I saw it crumpled up but it moved. It was a swan.

Walking past Rosemary's mother's house after midnight everything grey under the streetlights, the only thing that is orange. Walking past white fences which are grey, orange brick which is darker grey, yellow brick which is lighter grey, grass which is blue-green almost black.

Redbrick. Brick should be red. They don't even have the right brick here.

They? We.

She has a duvet, Rosemary I mean. I felt it and it was inside, something clumped together. I looked at the label and it said RAMIE. We used to have sheets. Nylon they stretched around the bed ends like the swimming costume lining. Then we got a duvet well I did, my parents still preferring sheets and heavy blankets liking the weight on them. My duvet was light was filled with something light that bounced back like skin. Rosemary's RAMIE is heavy as blankets, but in patches. Between the clumps are parts that are just outsides and it does not warm me those two cotton sheets. Still it is better to be cold like this like the art with torn bits, like the chipped mugs. It is a gap that asks to be crossed. When I cross it I know I have changed from.

But I know about the grey in the orange light. In a car the shadows flick across. In a room the shadows turn across the ceiling each time a car turns by with its orange lights. Neither in Rosemary's close nor in my road do cars pass very often.

Walking to Rosemary's house after midnight I pass
S
E
X
I do not go under the underpass. Though it looks deserted I am frightened. What am I taught to fear?

Dip, dip, they say, the swans. Swans are mute. They have no need to say anything else.

Instead I go over the road where the occasional car goes by so fast that it is much more likely to kill me.

(I do not really do any of this.)

July

Railings

Rosemary is having a party.
A party means clothes.

The money from the cattery is left each week in an envelope inside the feed bin. I never see the woman any more.

Summer builds. It stops. It doesn't. It goes slow. Have you seen the way clouds get in July? Solid, almost. Pushed across the sky. But not stopping, no.

Railings, over the road, joyful. Railings on the New Town footbridge. Through them the sun, cutting, underneath, the cars. The tarmac bounces, rebounds. This is sexy: their speed their vibrations through me, the tarmac path suspended the ear-filling noise everything. Sun under seagulls' wings, gold under.

Over the footbridge the station. I can never get there. The ticket machines a mystery.

Nothing ever stops.

CND in the city centre. A rowan tree in its square left soil from concrete. Beneath the paving stones. The wind lifts each bunch of berries in turn, in a circle. You can see the way the wind moves. Things give it body. It is always there.

Greenpeace Against Sizewell B

Between the concrete blocks I have on my new blouse, yellow, only a bit lopsided. I made it. That fastening at the neck I could never. Collars are difficult to sew. I go into Woolworths. Today my blouse has short sleeves. A handful of dolly mixture, in the palm, out the door.

The geological foundation comprises Norwich Crag Formation and Red Crag Formation bedrock of Pleistocene age above Eocene London Clay. The Crag deposits predominantly consist of medium dense and dense sands with thin layers of clay and silt and fossiliferous shelly horizons. The Crag strata extend to a depth of 200 feet (60 metres) below ground level.

Pick n' mix: they all taste the same colour: buttercup, pink, peach, no blue. Nothing is blue in nature, nothing that can be food.

The foundations for the reactors and associated boilers are provided by a reinforced concrete raft 8 feet (2.4 metres) thick, founded on the sand with a designed net bearing pressure of 3.5 tons per square foot. The biological shields are 100 feet (30.5 metres) high and vary between 10 and 14 feet (3 and 4.3 metres) thick. The composite steel and reinforced concrete cap above each reactor is 12 feet (3.7 metres) thick. Both reactors were housed in a single building to achieve savings in building costs.

Their sweet middle eyes brown black like daisies no not in nature but in a garden.

The turbine house is a steel framed, aluminium clad building 380 feet (115.8 metres) long, 160 feet (48.8 metres) wide and 90 feet (27.4 metres) high, with a reinforced concrete basement 26 feet (7.9 metres) deep. The foundations are provided by isolated bases and strip footings with a designed maximum bearing pressure of 3 tons per square foot.

Black-eyed susans.

I have seen things that look like that, a white ball on the poster about fungi, equally opaque. Unknowable as sex, a soft egg, balls: that word, something to do with men?
(It is called puffball fungi/It is the reactor containment building.)

I like that they taste of bland.

The pumphouse which supplied the main turbines with 27 million gallons of cooling water per hour drew sea water from an intake structure about 1,350 feet (410 metres) offshore via twin 10 feet (3 metres) diameter tunnels. This water was returned to the sea through similar tunnels discharging 350 feet (107 metres) offshore.

I'd like to be dolly mixture. Because I'd like to be, I know I'm not.

It is designed to withstand the impact of a fully-loaded passenger aircraft.
(I have never been on one of those.)

Each generation a little more terrified than the last. And too ashamed to tell.

The station was officially opened on 7 April 1967 by Commander The Earl
of Stradbroke, RN, the queen's Lieutenant of Suffolk.

But on the pavement a £10 note quite innocent just like that, crisp
from the dispenser. I am blessed! I've never had it so good though I've
had it sometimes: the undercharging by 5p, the rounding down, the
extra thing thrown in but never this yes I am so blessed!

Liven Up Your Classics!

The perfect wardrobe need be no more than a small collection of clothes.
Once you've chose that colour, stick to it for all your major buys.

(Must I stay boring for them?)

I am what is good to change from.

The simple stylishness of a skirt and loose jacket responds to your mood.
(Could it be anger?)

I am staying as small and uninteresting as possible.

There are twelve individual items of clothing giving more than thirty-six
different possibilities of combining them. Not one style for each person but several
styles for everybody.

This is both an act of pride and of humility.

A vital white shirt in either silk or polyester can transform an outfit.

I need transforming. I am transforming. I am never what I am.

Whether you are seeking a job or furthering your education, now you have the
exciting opportunity to wear what you want, to find your own style and learn how

to express your personality through the clothes you choose.

I want to change from day to evening. I don't even need to change my clothes. I can accessorise.

An executive-style suit may be appropriate for a legal secretary but too officious in a travel agency.

I want to be change.

If your job discourages trousers substitute another skirt to the plan.

It is possible to change. It is possible to choose to change. It is necessary to change from one woman to another. Woman is what is changeable. Everything is only a garment.

The perfect wardrobe need be no more than a small collection of garments. Don't let a small budget prevent you from dressing well.

Who, though, if I can be many?

Because you are in a uniquely free period of your life with youth entirely on your side you can wear the kind of zany clothes you can't get away with in ten years' time.

And how can I inhabit each sincerely?

A smashing sweater livens up your favourite jeans. A navy wool sweater can

be accessorised to take you out in the evening or for smarter daytime functions. The
rich wool American turtleneck. The wool must be wool or the best imitation. The
shoes, not seen here, are navy.

My current jeans are sincere. They fit me. They are a little uncomfortable, reminding me of their authenticity. Nothing is made exactly for me. That is how it should be.

A vogue for ripped jeans.
(Distressed?)
The classic jeans are neither ripped nor worn.
(Jeans. Pant.)
Style doesn't tolerate artificial fibres.
(Could beauty have better commerce than with honesty?)

What is a classic?
Now that fashion no longer dies each season, neither old nor new... A classic,
at the risk of appearing dull, is acceptable everywhere.

In any case I am not there yet.

Court

I knock on the door of the white bungalow on the ridge but the woman from the cattery isn't there. I leave her a note. 'I can't look after the cats I am on jury service. I have to go on jury service. It is legal. I don't know how long this lasts. It depends on the case.'

What else can I do?

Rosemary's party is at the end of the month.

The court is between the Old Town and the New Town. I walk very early to the bus stop by the supermarket in Rosemary's estate, on the post by the underpass

S

E

X

Now I pass it every day.

She is asking the boy from the house by the plantation to her party. Or do I mean man. I say, Rosemary, I can make you a dress.

The bus to the courts has breakfast radio on. Every day, the DJ talks to lovers. The seat patterns are violent, hard plush like in cinemas. They prickle the back of my legs.

My legs are bare.

The pattern for Rosemary's dress is from the 1920s. It has straps and is tight

over the bust then it is loose. At the bottom it gathers in and there are large fabric roses. The dress should be black. The roses should be pale pink.

(It is not really from the 1920s but from a play about them.)

The bus is singing: a choir ups a half-tone then half a tone more as its big brakes draw to a stop.

(Or is it screaming?)

It is cheap to make the dress out of two colours of lining material which is not silk but which it gestures towards. Lining material is honest because it does not convince. In lining material Rosemary can be beautiful but not too much. The material apologises for her beauty. But, as Rosemary is already beautiful, anything I do with the lining material does not matter.

The bus lets me off at the library, which is square and grey. Not many people at this end of town, grey paving between here and the New Town shopping centre. There are also two cashpoints where people queue. This is public space.

Rosemary takes off her t-shirt so I can measure her. I knew already she isn't wearing any bra. She takes off her skirt. She is wearing tiny ivory pants. Something about them is satin, but not quite. Blurred. On the front, something like seed pearls stitched on.

The concrete here is pale elephant hide. The road here is for buses. It is not a road. There's a track on each side where cars go. A bump in the middle to slow them. Like all bumps, it's sexy. I don't know if it's male or female.

Her side elastics don't dig in but rest over her hipbones, triangles of air beneath.

The court is between the New Town and the Old Town. By the bus station there is a caff where I have breakfast the first day: bacon sandwich and cappuccino, coffee with squirty cream on. At lunchtime I can walk in the New Town where there is boots the chemist superdrug woolworths nationwide marks and spencer wh smith bhs tesco c&a littlewoods. There is clarks martin's and the co-op and some shops without big names. This walking at lunchtime is what I enjoy most about the case.

She stretches her arms. Her breasts pull up, are triangles, her nipples not round but pyramid: at the ends small holes to black, the dimples of her elbows.

The court is old, perhaps. I buy a magazine walking here. I refuse to swear on the bible. The magazine shows me film stars wearing fashion. There are also beauty tips. I read it at lunchtime.

I put one arm under Rosemary's left arm, and the other under her right to catch the tape measure round her back.
There are small blonde hairs on her breasts, she smells of eggshells.

In court I wear the black skirt the black sweater a white blouse. It is hot so I take off the black sweater. (I wore the hat and the gloves on the bus but I took them off when I got here.
It seemed more serious than church. We are to listen carefully to the facts.)

The tiny hairs that cover her body breathe air between us.

126

I can feel them on my skin. At the other end of these hairs, she can feel me too.

Her arms raised, elastics catching on her hip bones make dark a gap down the front of her pants. The seed pearls.

The glass in the windows is wavy. Outside the court, trees bend without sound. It must be old then.

I have missed some of the facts looking at them—

When I kneel to measure her legs, there are the pearls up close, little black holes in them, and the thread, the holes in her nipples, the thread is not tight to the fabric, the elastic is not tight to her body.

Rosemary needs nothing tight.

—and also looking at Rosemary.

Rosemary moves. The tape moves.

Ah yes the man in court has taken a car and driven it without permission. It is his friend's car. It was early morning before breakfast time. He was stopped by the police. He was driving on the wrong side of the road. But because it was early morning no one else was driving on the road and no one was hurt. Because he had been arrested for driving before, he had to go to court.

I am very close now.

Nothing happened.
Nobody was harmed.

With her arms down she looks a bit more normal.

The jury has already agreed that the man in court is guilty.

I don't mind that he is guilty but I don't like that he is going to be punished.

Being only recently eighteen I am the youngest person on the jury.

Nothing happened.

I don't like that people are going to be punished.

Electric Blue For Blondes!

Vogue knows chic begins with a good body.

I am happy to be here at the shops—happy, not to choose, not having the money to choose—but to see choice. Happy for there to be choice, happy to find what choice I might be right for, happy to be able to say I can choose even if I cannot choose. I do not have even this choice elsewhere.

Women—especially those with style—gain enormous pleasure from choosing clothes.

There are blondes, brunettes and redheads. Then there is skin tone. Then there is style.
Peachy pink for instance is a warm yellow-based colour, while shocking pink is a cool, blue-based one.
What am I?

Some parts of my body are good some are bad some are unmentionable. Or rather some I don't know if they're good or bad. Or rather, there are some that must be bad because I cannot mention them.

I would like a t-shirt in every colour. I am beginning to collect them: red orange yellow green blue indigo, the rainbow. Which should I choose first?

(Black and white are not colours.)

SHOULDERS: should be approx 1 inch (2.5cm) wider than hips.
FAULT: Round face; avoid…

Cool electric blue for blondes.
All the people who aren't white come under '*brunette*'.
The electric substation has no windows. I am like it.
My skin is carefully concrete. It looks inward.
What am I? I am 'brunette'. I am not quite 'short'. I am 'small'. I am not 'thin'. I am not quite 'fat'. I do not have a 'round face'.
Rosemary has a round face, but there is no fault in it.
I'm not sure which is my face shape.
Rosemary is not watchable.

To illustrate, a photo of a brown-haired girl wearing the wrong colours. *Wishy washy pastels only weaken her features.*

The models are the same age as me but not at all like me. They don't look like anyone my age. They are 'beautiful'. I am not 'ugly' but beautiful is what I am not.
Not many girls are beautiful, but there is only beautiful and not beautiful.
Many girls are not.

The dirt on my school bag is an outrage. It is not to do with me. How can I make sure everyone knows it?
It is from putting it down a lot.

My mother says, make *sure it's real leather*.

I buy a belt. It is electric blue. It is soft as fabric. I think it is real leather but it is not.

I did not know it was wrong before she told me.

I am in any case not a blonde.

I try dressing how they dress, the models in the photos. I'm not right. I don't understand how. I look at other girls but no one really looks like a model, not even beautiful girls who are tall and thin. I don't know what the other girls are like. I don't know how they look like they look like themselves. They look quite ordinary, then not. When I dress like a model I stand out. I don't want to stand out. But I am also not one of the girls by the bus stop who are another kind of different. I don't know where that difference is. If I could find it out, I could look like them. If I looked like them I would be one of them. (Which comes first?) And would that be good or bad?

I wear my cardigan backwards, its buttons along my spine. I belt it with the blue belt. It is not leather but I ignore this.

I wear a blue beret in the heat. It matches my belt.

be individual!
be inventive!
repurpose!

On the racks in the chain stores in town, the same old clothes. They could be wrapped tucked pinned perhaps. They could be worn backwards upside down. I could buy painters' dungarees cleaners' tabards boys' school trousers tiny children's sweaters.

Rosemary says, *You dress arty.*
That was not my intention.
I am not the right shape for this book.

Bus

Walking to the bus stop to go to the court I have my walkman. I am listening to Madonna *I am a material girl*. I recorded it from the radio.

I don't know if I like it but other people like it so.

Something tinny in my ears. And something that tastes like tin.

And inside my nose I can still smell the cat food.

Or maybe it got into the walkman.

By the underpass—

S

E

X

—there is a dead thing by the side of the road. No one moves it.

It was a fox. It might have been a cat, but I think it unlikely.

It is bigger.

(Whose job to move it?)

I pass the dead thing every day and every day it grows flatter and wider.

Between the court in the morning and the court in the afternoon I eat lunch on a bench. I buy it from boots the chemist. It is sandwiches in a triangle pack. I am special now, like an office worker and because I have a kind of job my mother gives me money for sandwiches. For the first time I am hungry because I have the money to meet it.

The green stuff under the bridge smells of something quite particular, growing and rotten at the same time.

It is hot by the court but there are trees. The trees thrash. The chestnuts are heavy with leaves. Each branch moves separately. The tree is many all at once. All of them say nothing.

I buy a sandwich from boots. My sandwich is prawn. Prawn is special. I am special because I eat prawn.

I am thinking about the cat.

The bench is around the tree.

Under the tree small things like cigarette ends and hair elastics coke cans and the plastics from sandwich triangles and more between the cobble stones, smaller things: safety pins earring backs paper clips.

A man sits on the bench beside me. He could sit on the opposite side of the tree but he does not. I do not know what he means by this. He unwraps his sandwiches. I can see them and they are cheese.

(Cheese is not special. Egg is not special. Prawn costs more, but not a lot more.)

I peel mine back.

The trick is to put it in your mouth without breathing in and smelling its release.

The concrete must be hot on the bridge right now.

The man looked at me and I looked this way and that as though I thought he might have been looking at someone else which I knew he wasn't. I had been looking at him too but not in the eyes. I had admired his tight checked shirt his neat head. I had noticed the belly that stuck out from his neat torso and had already forgiven him for it. His big body would be right in other circumstances; here it is an inconvenience. It is brown and strong and big, beautiful even—he is perhaps a lifeguard, a tennis coach—but bent over all the things that go to make it— sandwiches home-made a packet of crisps an egg a chocolate bar—it is disgusting. What men need is disgusting, what big men need, what they don't mind making themselves from.

Looking is a fault in me. Why mustn't I be the one doing the looking? I am always putting myself in the situation where men can look at me. Or maybe that is a normal situation and I am not putting myself there at all. One day one of them speaks to me. Perhaps. I have no idea how to speak to one of them or what one of them would say to me. In the meantime I am quite satisfied.

I look away and see the trees move, but what I hear is cars.

Heart

A sign:

FOR WHERE YOUR TREASURE IS THERE YOUR HEART IS ALSO.

FOR WHERE YOUR TREASURE IS THERE YOUR HEART IS ALSO.

How do clothes get into words? The words are something that comes into my mouth and fills it up so I can't breathe almost. They don't seem to come from outside. They seem to come from inside me as though putting on the clothes I could also bring them out of my mouth like a string of magician's flags: someone might even think that I had spoken.

Texture: a knobbly slub linen suit. Soft grey pigskin over a delicate knit sweater and a soft silk shirt in
   Apricot (a texture and a colour).
   Over and—
Lacy knit cotton vest with inset shoulder pads makes a warm pretty extra layer.
   —under.
   The clothes so bright, so

I mustn't think about clothes. Not if I want to be a serious woman. But I can't think of a serious woman, not how she looks. Does she wear no clothes? I look at the clothes without thinking of clothing and they're something else, I don't know what. Perhaps a serious woman wears a blue suit. This is how adults are: a blue suit. It is polyester, I can feel it almost. It is the same as the suit I wear working in the estate agent and, working there, I know I am not a serious woman but I cannot imagine another way to be grown-up.

I cannot imagine a woman being serious.
But I can now see the nude lining inside the blue suit. Lining material.

FOR WHERE YOUR TREASURE IS THERE YOUR HEART IS ALSO.

Looking at fashion magazines like looking at sex.

Lift

At lunchtime between the court in the morning and the court in the afternoon I go into a small dark shop selling gift wrap and Victorian-style china dolls. I am pleased by its novelty.

It's in an old building—some brick some timber—and I walk into it and the door is low and there's a step down. Inside it is cool and dark there are rows of dolls on the shelves looking like Victorian dolls with faces made of china but their hair is nylon and they smell like Sindy.

The goods in this shop are not authentic.

I pick up a doll and its head falls to one side of the body. It is cloth and the head is heavy. It doesn't close its eyes like a plastic doll but looks just the same. I prop it back up. On the counter a stand of brooches and earrings. I turn it: dragonflies wooden painted; bees, silver with dirt rubbed makes them look old. I like to pick things up feel their weight put them back like I am making a choice but it's wiped clean each time so I can make it again and again. I pick up a rainbow eraser a roll of stickers which are of cats a sheet of old-style collage cut outs what are they for? a pair of brass earrings with swallows dangling a mug to see the price on the bottom it is ugly art deco imitation then back to the stand, a brooch like a deer in mirror plastic, a brooch like a pair of lips, the bee again the fox brooch in the same hand I palm the bee slip it down my sleeve feel its pin scratch my wrist replace the fox walk slowly to the door elevating my left hand to pick up a roll of decorative tape a handmade bowl, the door tinkles but it did that when I came in.

The women behind the counter labelling something, I don't know what.

I pin the bee to my lapel only two streets later. And I go back to the court.

Things I don't talk about:
If I don't buy anything. If nobody can see me. If nobody can hear me.
(Taking things is not buying them.)
(Doing things then not saying is not doing.)
(Not talking is not being.)

What I take is in any case always very small.

Undercover

Each piece of clothing calls to me: this one, this one! I could be any of them. I choose. I pick up—

That latest thing that is so pretty.

—a red silk slip that is in fact made of polyester.

(Furs of course are liked for their wickedly luxurious feel as well as for being status symbols.)

How do you get close, close enough for it. And when you are close enough what do you say?

(The extremely feminine woman who adorns herself with the country look is more often to be found in the heart of town than down on the farm. The woman who wears the country look should not be confused with the country girl who works on the land. She has as much man-appeal as the more womanly female and an apparently unwitting sexiness.)

The man on the bench. (The boy in the house by the plantation (or is he a man?).) If I could properly imagine what it does inside his trousers, then I could move it without touching him.

(Resist the temptation to put it with very tight black or leather clothes. You don't want to look like a maitresse.)

I've been in worse places in which to change: the dolls we had, plastic, always naked, their hair cut odd, or matted with heat or dirt. That's how we are. Sometimes a new doll came but that's how they ended up. Some girls had twenty of these dolls, thirty, to bear witness to them. None ended up any different. I knew there was something wrong with this encounter.

The purest possible fabrics (cotton, crêpe de Chine, and silk).

The dolls were pink and plastic. I am pink but not hard and smooth.
I am wrong.
The dolls have nothing.
Inside which there are pink wrinkled things inside which something darker again.
There is nothing this can be compared to. Even the body covers it up with hairs as soon as it starts to show.

These are the hidden clothes, the clothes you keep closest to you that nevertheless may be on show.

There is no silk only nylon. One silk bra in the sale bin. It is pale blue I think they call it duck egg though duck eggs are greener. It is tiny, each unsupported triangle framed with lace. It is like nothing I've seen before. It would not fit me but it might fit Rosemary. I take it with the slip back to the changing room.

My body its own pornographic object.

Change

The woman in the changing room trying on underwear, her stomach surging upward like a ship, her cotton knickers the wrong shape—no she is the wrong shape—gathered around her flat buttocks, screwed round her waist, bagging over the flatiron of her vulva.

I am my stomach. I am careful with it, always wary as I can't control it. There it is around the top of my trousers not obtrusive unless I wear something tight. But then it is. So I do not wear something tight. It is still there only no one knows anything about it.

To be this middle point which is not controlled and has no function is wrong.

It is exciting we're both so ugly.

It is exciting to be so wrong.

I take off the trousers I dyed. I wanted them so very much to be a different colour. I had bought red trousers which were immediately wrong. I am not the sort of person who wears red: I am of course the sort of person who wears green. I bought pale green dye a colour not in nature but the colour of green cake icing or green toilet paper or maybe the inside of cow parsley stalks but mostly a colour only also called *pastel green* and pastel is also the name of a sweet, or *mint green* but not like the plant, like mints you suck. The trousers dyed ok but shrank up to my ankles. I'd stripped out the red with colour remover first. Then I put the new colour in, the pale green. This meant I had to boil the trousers twice.

To have style is to make a little difference.

It is difficult to make something different.
It is easier to make myself different.

My mother said I shouldn't do it would spoil a good new pair of trousers. But Rosemary is wearing the leather skirt she washed. There is a split. She has taped it with electrical tape, waist to hem. She laughs. On her, it looks right.

Then I am carrying the bra wrapped in tissue paper down the street. It is in a plain plastic bag. There could be anything in there.

Undercover reveals all!

It is so small; I could have stolen it.

Cherry

I wish now that I had some the cherries in chocolate like the ones Rosemary brought. I buy some off the market in the New Town with writing in Polish. I bought some material for a blouse there. I can't find the clothes I like in the New Town, clothes like in the magazine. The material I bought is lemon 100% cotton. Synthetics are wrong but it was stiff and so is the blouse I made so stiff that afterwards I didn't know how I'd wanted it. I made the waist too narrow not much but just a bit because I want my waist to be narrower not much just a bit more than it is now. I knew as I was making the blouse that the waist was too narrow but I couldn't make myself make it fit.

I cannot tell why my body does not obey my clothes.

The chocolates I bought on the market weren't like Rosemary's, the liquid tasting sharp and smelling of nail polish remover. But it is good to eat them because I remember Rosemary's chocolates.

(Blouse is a funny word in any case. Out loud I might say 'blousse'. Can't help myself.)

When Rosemary comes to my house I took the chocolates off the shelf and put them in the cupboard.

The collar was extra stiff with two layers of the stiff lemon fabric sewn together and stiffener between. It stuck up and that's what I'd wanted it to do but I found I didn't want to look like I imagined or that what I'd imagined was perhaps the blouse not me in it. It stands up well on its own. I don't wear it much after a first couple of times. I don't like what I've made of myself.

Later Rosemary said where are the chocolates let's eat them. I said, oh I don't know I looked in a few cupboards and eventually brought them out, oh I said I'd forgotten them.

On the market I buy 3 yards of black lining material 2 yards of pink. Now I can make something for Rosemary to dislike.

I wanted the chocolates but also I wanted Rosemary to stay.
Rosemary wanted the chocolates.

Makeup: The 7 Deadly Sins

Even in the magazines women look wrong: boiled and red and round in close-up. I don't want to look like them. I don't want to look like anything. But I don't want to look like a man, and what else is there to look like?

On the shelves, an eyeshadow is telling me it is IMPORTANT TO. A cold cream is telling me to TAKE CARE OF.

Our pointless faces. Not even beautiful. How do they still exist?

Green is my colour.
I have chosen.
I buy:
a makeup palette with mint green eyeshadow, very pale like water in the stream, like watercolour. Going on though it's powdery, is paler than even my skin. The lipstick is transparent, greasy. In the palette it looked red. I apply it with the very small brush (provided), the rough round sponge on the tiny stick for the eyeshadow. I stroke it over three times to make sure. Nothing sticks. Then there is bottle green eyeliner. The water colours. The red poppy.

Liptint
Lip
Tint
But I am looking in the wrong direction. Rosemary doesn't look like

the fashion magazines: she looks like she does not need them.

What is it like to be one of those women? I can see them but I can't feel it.
(What is it like to be Rosemary?)

There is no full-length mirror in my house.
Is there any way I can see myself all the way round?

They are all outsides.

It's not her makeup: her face is expensive.

I go to Rosemary's house. Her mother is out. I am sleeping over.

And I see it once, the heron.

There is something about sleeping over. It is important. It is important
for me to be at Rosemary's all night. It is what? Possession?

In the morning, on my way to the cattery. Standing in the stream. On one leg
like they're meant to.
I stop. It is important not to move.

What did I imagine? (Whatever I imagine it is not the same: where
does this imagining come from?) There was me but also some friends
of Rosemary—boys also—some friends of her sister they were younger.
We lay on our fronts in our sleeping bags all pointing toward the TV,

not touching. We had crisps. We watch a video. The women inside wear orange. They are in prison. Someone has told us that at some point there is sex. This is what the boys here are waiting for.

On my bike, one foot to the ground.

There was the boy from the house by the plantation. I try not to look at him. As though looking were catching. Catching what. I don't want him to look back. How do I look?

We do not see, we do not see nature like this: big, impressive, often.

They had to wait too long for the sex. The film was quite serious. That means the sex was not straight away. They got bored and turned it off. I was watching it. I wanted to go on. I didn't know what to say. I knew not to say. I knew I shouldn't be so serious. But I only knew it at that moment, not before.

I was already too serious. And, as though serious were a movement, not a mood, I found I could not stop.

I mean I don't.

There's something about where it crosses, the film. I'm not safe. It's not the same with the others. When I see something it crosses into me. Everything crosses into me from all sides. I try to pretend it doesn't, so that I can say it doesn't. But it does. I don't know what to do with that. I am embarrassment.

I stop because you stop for nature, when it's big.
In my sleeping bag, I fold parts of myself away.

Nature does not visit us often in large cell clusters moving all at once head beak wings tail.

I look at Rosemary to see the same thing. I don't find it. She is laughing, her face toward the boys. She switches the film off. We play spin the bottle. Rosemary's sister's friends leave. We smoke cigarettes in Rosemary's back garden. I do all this as waiting. She has a bottle of vodka.

In another country it would not be big. But there are no big animals in England, except farm animals: cows, pigs—that behave just like you expect them to, don't go outside their fields.

What am I waiting for?

But it's not cow country here.

And later she was asleep her hair spilled across the carpet, her head missing the pillow, everything missing spilled cigarette ends crisps mini rolls fagash bottles.

A run-over badger by the motorway.
Sometimes a fox.

Fold in parts of myself away. Fold into her around her. Is she awake?

The sleeping bag is silky, like that inside skin. Strange that feeling, that inside self, soft but muscled, tight. The sleeping bags are orange. No, orange on the outside, bright, silky, and inside lighter coral, the inside of a swimsuit, nude. It is bigger than me so I can fold it round me, between my legs, flesh on flesh. Asleep in the streetlight nothing is flesh coloured. Yes inside like the sleeping bag but ridged: muscle, bones almost, wet.

The hare is designed for danger. Most animals here are.
There are no large predators left in the UK. Not animals anyway.
I have never seen an owl.
Sometimes I think I hear one. I might be wrong.

In films it's always the first time. But no one minds.
Here they mind.
You can repeat a video over and over again.
But, anyway.

It is a very slow moment. No one moves. The heron. Its orange eye.

And Rosemary in the morning, flushed from the nylon sleeping bag. The invalid offering of her face, round and white and for once I can begin to describe it. That's because it's almost ugly, a biscuit on the floor. Crisp crumbs stuck in her hair, a squashed lager can on the carpet. One of us must have slept on it.

Things I don't talk about:
To put my hand on.
To put my hand in.

Did I or not?

I look away from what I might have done until I don't know.

What did I do?

It looks straight at me, the heron.

Or so I imagine.

And then it goes.

What is it I have done to her?

What is it I am doing (am I still doing it? I don't know)?

Does she know what I am doing to her?

It is so big in the air, how can it survive this country? Even in the air it is too

big.

We don't mention going to her house again.

August

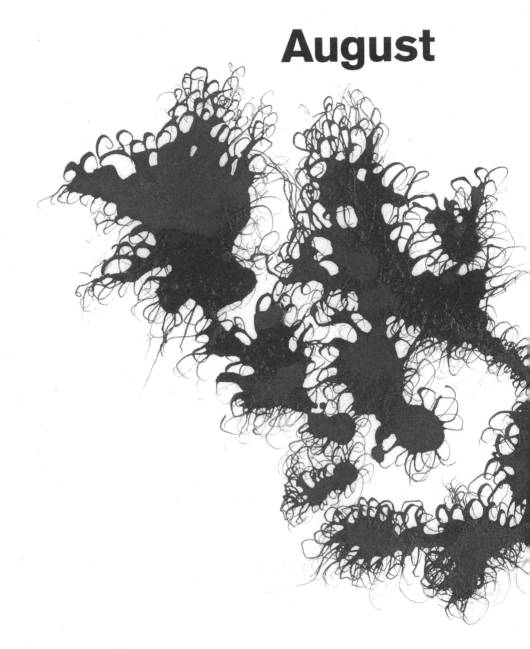

Snaps

August: the clouds tall like buildings.

Some things happen only in memory. That's where story's made. I remember the last day like snapshots but not. I mean not in pictures but in something that feels the same. I can't see myself in them not even other people just a bit of them perhaps a colour of a shirt, the corner of a forehead. Also the feel of a jumper or grass or something, the pressure of wind or sun, the smell of hot tarmac green water whatever. A snap.

Second-hand Rose finds fashion in other people's memories!

Moths with blue topwings, red underneath. Too many of them. Do they eat something? Your clothes? They've done it already. It's the grubs that eat them. Maybe only wool though. There's one wrapped in spiderweb in a gate corner you can only just see the colour. It's husky, light, dried out, drained a small parcel it got caught I guess.

Second. Hand.
I don't mind that they were other people's clothes once.

I don't like to pose for pictures.

White moths like reverse vision.
How do I look?

The bats do something scientific in the dark.

There were other times. They had different colours then. Photo colours from ten years ago are different, unnatural. Were real colours different too? Those times were also silent; I see a film of my grandparents on holiday somewhere at the seaside, laughing, talking without making any noise at all. Did they look like that their reds coral and their greens blue and their yellows lemon?

Second-hand Rose knows that older, more established communities tend to discard better quality clothing while city sales tend to be filled with man-made undesirable fibres. Pure wool, hand knits, wool crêpe, tweed, gaberdine, men's suiting and crisp cotton.

Don't touch the caterpillars: their hairs can poison you.

My gran looks different that's why it was a long time ago. They all look different the women with strange dresses their hair all piled up on top of their heads their lips pale their eyes dark. The men look more or less the same just the colours different. My dad has some clothes from then they really are different colours— beige and orange. They are artificial but the people are different colours too.

The fashion detail is the chameleon effect. It always pays to pay attention.

Don't touch the millipedes, only because they are disgusting.

It was only two years before I was born.
Groundsel.
Docks blood coloured. The seeds of everything are like that, dirtily round the edges.

Not much further back and it's black and white. And that's nothing to do with anyone.

70% acrylic 30% wool rayon nylon polyester polycotton vinyl. I look and look but I don't find 100% wool. I have heard of cashmere but I have never seen it. I feel the word instead: cash. mere. = expensive. small.

We are not people to write stories about but we have been photographed. Only the things we did in the photographs were worth seeing including weddings holidays school outings church outings anniversaries christenings: everything else we did was not.

I know summer is turning now.

What is a photo album?
For remembrance.

I kept one once. It had a rainbow cover, for every image a drawn square. Obediently, I filled the space and on the lines beneath wrote what I thought they showed. This year I burnt it. I don't remember that I was those words. These neither.

Clever anticipation means that all the surprises are happy ones!

Nothing much happens here. Not even anything bad enough for us to tell.

Everything's happening elsewhere anyway. The valley is not going anywhere for the summer.

This is what my parents want for me: that nothing should happen. What cannot be said to have happened cannot have happened. I should be nothing you can make a story out of. Who could blame them?

Hospital

Things I don't talk about:

Sunday is dads shouting at their children in all the houses in the village, and in mine.

After all it is the only time they are with them.

At lunch they turn another way. They can only turn. How can this go on? How can it not go on? Because it does go on even as they pretend it does not. But it is not pretence. Because how can it go on, this shouting at the dinner table while eating, while eating long green beans and roast pork which must be cut up small because of dryness in order to be chewed. There is no place for shouting here, for shouting with mouths full. But there is no place for anything else. Nothing is taking place then. Or words that must be ignored.

We must not get too close. This is what words are for.

There is always something not being done.

Sunday is also for the hospital.

I am not thinking about Gran. I am still thinking about Rosemary's party. Rosemary's party could be the first time, perhaps the boy from the house in the plantation, the boy Rosemary has invited.

Gran wants me to massage her face. Her skin is loose yet very close to the bone. The wrinkles push over her skull. Whichever way I push them, they don't go away. The face cream doesn't sink in, she just looks more shiny. I don't dare go near her neck.

I think of him only because I can't think of anyone else.

How did either of us get myself into this situation?

How do we look? I don't mean how do we look today, I mean how do we end up looking like this? Like that? Any of us?

(The thing that isn't. I mean I can't imagine. They say it stands up. Does it or does it not have hairs on?)

I mean I don't see any old women who look good.

I mean I don't see any old women who look like anything at all.

Some of them look like clowns women I mean hair dye and face paint. There's nothing they can do about the wrinkles.

Songs

When I recorded the songs on the tape. I wasn't looking for any song in particular but there was one I liked, though I missed the DJ's voice, the song's beginning. I listen to it over. I embed the words. I think it's an old song, my parents' generation. It's difficult to find that sort of stuff now. You have to make the most of it while you're hearing. If you don't know the title. I don't find it again.

The songs I like best have something plastic about them, and white, like the plastic skin paint that peels on Rosemary's fence, like the white of her kidney dressing table where the strip round the edge is loose and peels too. Underneath is brown. It's wood even though it's compressed chips. Does this count as nature? Whatever, brown is under everything.

I repeat it to myself as birdsong.
I play it in my head as I walk,
without the walkman,
from my house, to the plantation, to the ring road, to the bus stop.
All winter past the brown fields with white bones.

What I can't do is remember a song when I don't know what it is yet.
It's not a song I remember, it's a song about memory.
There's nowhere I can look up the words. I can't ask them to the air.
I never hear it again.

I didn't think it was coming through the radio. It was something to do with my mother at home, doing the washing up. It was about leaving. Me on the swing—I heard the words clearly—she in the kitchen. But no one was going anywhere: I didn't think about that.

That was a past song but there are songs that are future. Even when they're sad the tune's upbeat. That's what 'adult' must be. It sounds distant. In order to become an adult I am changing. See me move to the estate get a job, wear a navy blue skirt suit smoke buy my own cigarettes take them out of my handbag go to the pub on a Friday get highlights wear frosted lipstick, take the bus to work ladder my tights have a spare pair handy wear heels do my nails carry a handbag to keep the tights and cigarettes in get a blow-dry lose my keys order a white wine spritzer save coins for the gas meter wait for the weekend have a boyfriend have— that. Or do it. It's a matter of a year. Or it could be now, if I don't go to university. The songs are detergent. Not natural, but better.

PARTY!

PARTY! Is about play and about sex, so you've got to show yourself off. PARTY! is about going places, looking brilliant at the opera, in the hotel, nightclubbing.

(Night.
Clubbing.
 The unfamiliar taste of the word.)

In the country there is no fashion.

Fantastic garlands!

Luckily for the party girl young, inexpensive designers use a lot of artificial fibres that don't show with the night lights.

Are there hunters here? I never see them.

Small dots work with large spots!

Only in the wood a sign: TRAPS.

Clothes that seem relaxed and comfortable in an urban environment can often look precious and out of place in a rural scene.

(Beauchamp Place.
Sloane Street.
New Bond Street.)

The Alternative Tux is the party girl who doesn't want to wear a frock.
It's perfect for a winter wedding or even, if differently accessorised, suitable for a funeral.

Can fashion come from us?
Might we be 'native'?

In 1988 the key word is confidence. Modern style assumes a certain modern assurance.
Apply your makeup to create a stunning effect. Dress to have fun and the chances are you can!

Dirt

The woman from the cattery has not called me.

It is my third morning when the man is on my bus. He gets on after me. He is the man in court I mean the accused. He is on the top deck. He passes me. I am sitting behind him. He does not look happy but he does not stop going to court. He could get down and get off, but he carries on going. He is on his own and he carries on going even though there is no one to make him. He does not look sad either. He looks just like everyone else.

(I am on the bus it bumps it goes down the hill quickly I sit at the front at the top it feels like sex.

If this is what sex feels like.)

I am on the bus to the court and they are playing the radio the same station that talks to lovers every morning. They play the top ten but not the song that has been banned. It has been banned because the words in it. I can't tell what the words might be. I am on the bus thinking about what they might be. The song might be like the songs the boys sing on the school bus and they call them rugby songs but they're not about rugby, they're dirty songs about women, or they are songs in which they call women by dirty words so that I don't know if the dirt is in the woman or the songs. The boys sing about *what every woman has* and call it dirty. Because they call it dirty I don't know what to do with this what

164

every woman has. Surely I don't have it, and surely my mother doesn't and Rosemary and Rosemary's sister because we do not seem to be dirty not like the songs. If we are women we have it and if we have what can be described in those words we can be put via those words into a dirty song. We do not use those words about ourselves but we do not use other words either so we cannot change them. *We know what we are, but know not what we may be.* Because we do not seem to be dirty to ourselves, having no other words, we must spend all our time ignoring what we have knowing all the time we have it. This is an effort. Or perhaps we are not women. In any case no one can tell if the song that is in the top ten is a dirty song after all because no one hears the words. So I don't know how any of us can tell what it's about. All the song tells me is that things can be banned.

I go the same way every day.

There are certain ways I can see myself. These are ways I have been described. There are others that have not even been described to me.

I have not heard from Rosemary for some time.

Catch

Things I can't talk about:

It is very quiet but all noise, very quiet noise. If you lie on the bridge you can hear them; that's the easiest. The noise closer to the ground and you don't know what it is you're hearing if it's the cars on the ring road that gets into everything or other human machines—

The New Town at lunchtime. Into the chemist's (so light outside), inside the light is yellow. There is nothing bright about it. I slip the lipstick against my palm, feel it streak against my wrist, into my sleeve: orange; it doesn't even suit me.

I have never been caught before.

—or is it the trees always moving also very small things moving under the ground and on top of the ground ants pulling leaves into holes also worms moving and birds the noise they make when they land on a branch it must be very little but still a noise or is it the noises flies and bees make with their wings anything that displaces air—

Out of the door the man caught my wrist. Old he was wearing a white thing not an apron or overall but a jacket thing like a waiter, well like pharmacists wear. Old I could have pulled could have run could have pushed him back. The corners of his mouth turned down like *this is worse for me than* his mouth on a hinge carved down, his wrinkles following the line of his mouth his eyes I don't look at.

—and also the noises of all small animals stepping and even of plants yes!
things growing that must make noises sometime moss expanding to crumble what
it grows on—

I make my eyes blank.

—also the sounds of spiders attaching pieces of web to things and of water
moving very slowly from one place to another not just the stream—

The words went away. I am talking but I cannot hear. How do I know
then that I am saying *I bought it yesterday, I bought it somewhere else.* I say
the same again not so he can hear me but so I can. I say *it didn't come from*
here. The old man turns me away. I can see something struggle in him.
He could call the police, he could hit me, he could look in my bag and
find my name he could have my name put down somewhere he could
look it up he could call my mother he could stop me going to university
he could shout but he does none of these things no he shoos me not to
come back. It was a shout, but swallowed. I don't know what stops him.
Disgust? I have changed into something that disgusts someone.

—also water everywhere how it gathers in the black rubber parts around car
windows after the night so drops eventually push together until big enough to form
a stream down the pane and also each blade of grass hitting against another—

How do I know what words I said? Did I think them?

167

I walk very fast to the outskirts of the centre of the town where there is an inner ring road. I walk very fast as though I am walking away though I know I am only walking in a circle. I can't walk away from here. Is it fear? But nothing is happening. Apart from the man, no one has seen me.

If no one tells, does it matter what has been seen?

—Also each leaf when the wind blows but also just because of the position of the tree how it grows very slowly and things are always moving yes all the time yes.

I had to go back to the court in any case.

Rock

Something is being buried.

Everyone agreed what the man had done but no one had seen him do it. One of the men on the jury said it didn't matter. Everyone agreed with him. I did not agree but.

(My dad is making a rockery. He has pieces of concrete. One of them has a wire in it. He buries it upside down so it looks more natural.)

On the ground small apples already, pick them up and they are full of wasps.
There is smoke far off.
Sometimes no smoke but its smell.
Some of the wasps are dead.

The top of the bus pushes against the leaves of the trees.
The wind. The trees snap back. Like dancing in the poem? No. Something violent.

(My dad puts plants in the rockery. They are blue. Their flowers are harsh. There are floppy sticky flowers that attract black bugs. They have striped skirts. I don't like to go near them in any way.)

At the end of the third day, the man is taken off to prison.

The flowers in the gardens are completely different. That's how you know they're gardens.

Candles outside when it's too light to need them. That'll do for the moths. Only for that. The trees still carrying on, not caring, all of them in different directions.

One of the butterflies is called 'burnt' something.
The crickets look like husks of things. They're dried up but still alive.

(You can get through the fence all along our garden. It is gappy. The bottom of it is rotting. My dad puts bushes in too but they never grow enough to fill the gaps.)

Some moths look like the bark of trees.
The grass seeds ripe now, and soft if you pull them through your finger. You pull them the wrong way and they splinter off. I said that before but it's easier now.

We saw something swimming once at the stream. An otter, or would that be wishful thinking. An animal, *not a fish*, perhaps. A water rat, whatever. Just not a fish.

The ducks lose their colour. The drakes I mean. They don't have sex any more. They all look like girls. Or they are pretending. Or they were pretending. Everything to do with sex looks like something.

After the court, I don't go back to the cattery.

Rosemary's Party

The fields on fire not that you see the fire, or you never see it close up. It is always across the fields on days the wind disappears, on the other side of the valley. And very soon it is over.

In the event Rosemary wears another dress. The roses are in any case sewn on badly.

I don't know what other dress she wears.

Something is being harvested. I don't know what.

I bring my mix tape to Rosemary's party.

Rosemary's party is at her mother's house.

The docks rusty, their ends crumbling, most of the berries red already. Everything rusting, oxidised, never really clean. That's what this country is: dirty. Always some mess somewhere I don't mean the earth I mean always some chicken wire or something you look over to see the view. Nothing proper. Always something like the post with

S

E

X

What spoils nature? We do. It is us. Even by seeing something, we're spoiling it already. The plants too, dirty, scrubby. They grow this way because of us. Everything's spoiled already. Nature grows to suit us. We are this land. There's nothing we can do to stop it.

I go because I was invited. I was invited some time ago and I have not been uninvited. At her door I think perhaps Rosemary is pleased to see me after all.

I see I am a strange thing specially now. Day-to-night: I wanted to change and I have changed. I have pulled the hairs out of my legs then rubbed them with oil to smooth them. New hairs already poke through the holes.

I wear Love Musc. I wear a top with no shoulders. I wear my mother's strapless bra. Its wires dig.
I must be sex.

Wait it is the yellow that has gone.

I look like I am going to a party.
When I arrive I realise this might be wrong.

They did it without us seeing.
They took away the sour smell.
Maybe it was a day we were not at the river.

I sit in one place in the party with a bottle of beer.
Because I say nothing it goes quickly.
Although it is empty I must keep hold of the bottle. I don't know why this helps.
What is left after is black earth.
(Nothing black in nature.)

As dark as nature gets then.

The coats are in Rosemary's bedroom. The drawer at the top, is pulled out and the formica strip has fallen off so the particleboard edges can be seen. It must snag her tights. In the top drawer, some scarves, some bottles of nail varnish in the corner, the satin knickers with the beads. How do I know? Because I look in it. On one of the beads a loose thread. I pull it to see what happens. What happens is it comes off. Obviously. The bead falls. I don't know where. It is no longer perfect.

There are flints in the black soil.
The remaining fields are blonde.

We only have the appearance of cohesion. Even each group. All we are doing is standing in the same room. Which cuts to another. The bathroom or something. Which is sudden. I like this jump of time. Cut the boring bits of the story, it's novel! Now there are parts coming up too close: the curtains, the bannister, but it's funny, that. Or someone's laughing anyway.

Could it be me?

The oats all lean down one way like fur.

If you slide your hand down the crack in Rosemary's sofa crumbs get in your nail.

I am sitting there drinking a bottle. I slide my hand because one hand is holding the bottle but the other does now know what to do.

There is sometimes something else, not often, but it's worth trying.

Sometimes fifty pee.

Under the sofa is wide black nylon webbing. It feels secure.

The webbing is the shape of people's buttocks, or maybe just that shape anyway. The sofa smells like old trouser. How do I know? I am near it.

The smooth veneered bones that stick out through the fabric at the arms' ends: no fingers.

I am lying on the floor looking under the sofa. I can see the crumbs. There is also another bottle or perhaps it is mine.

Is it nature?

After a while I'm in the corner. Probably nothing happened.

My mouth is dry.

I am folded into the corner. I can feel its hard ridge against my back, its gap. I can feel the bumpy wallpaper.

If you slide your nail under the lumps they come out. They are small pieces of wood. Sometimes they get stuck in your nail. Sometimes they go all the way under which is a splinter. It hurts, but it is still possible to provoke this.

Rosemary and her sister are listening to a tape. I know who this is but I have not listened before. I don't say I don't know. All the people are looking in front of them but not at each other. They all seem to understand something. It is 3 in the morning. I can see the clock which is digital and lights up. Rosemary has a stack of VOGUES by her bed. She uses it for a nightstand.

We never knew the name of the river.

I wear Love Musc. The man is taller than me. That's why I call him a man now. He is taller than I thought the boy by the swimming pool at the house by the plantation was. Men their strange large bodies their big shoes. Who made them that scale? We're scarcely human to them. My dad: short, is nothing to do with them either. Some men never were. *He took me by the wrist and held me hard.* We are in the room with the coats, a bedroom. He opens his mouth against mine, around mine because his mouth is bigger. My lips feel the bumps of his acne. He tastes of smoke.

I saw in a painting once the animals fleeing all with human faces the woods on fire.
But it was only a postcard.
It was necessary to peer very closely to see the detail.

He is not a man. He is only one year older, though his tall hard body is made to fool you.

See, seen, saw. Can't be unseen. Who can't unsee? It is not me because I am not looking at anyone. I can see, what, the wallpaper perhaps, the torn corner of the picture, its reflective glass.

It was not me did this. It was him.
Did what?

it

To look at something and, at the same time, to look away.
To see, and to make my eyes flat

175

So they can't read, so they see surfaces.
His hand.
Rosemary's hand. Mine.
To make a blank face like I don't understand.
To make a face that isn't even blank, that doesn't even show I am ignoring
something.

But who is seeing, me or Rosemary?

I am not even here.
And

It does not matter that it was in any case not me doing the doing.

(What mattered was the seeing.)

Why does neither of us think it is him?

I do nothing for myself or for other girls. I even harm them by example.

Why does neither of us think he matters?

In that space I look up at the trees. Like me they move but they say nothing.
There is some freedom in looking at the trees but I don't know what it is.
Why does a party always feel we are bad?

Train Dream

I dream I go into Topshop in the New Town but the street is steeper. I dream shops on the side streets I don't recognise. They are sinister. I dream I'm in Woolworths and I can't find the lipsticks. I always dream of bargains. Sometimes I dream I find them. Almost.

I don't dream of shopping anywhere else. It is still my town.

I sometimes dream of trying to leave.

The wind lifts the hair of the trees. You can see it right across the valley, you can see the shape of it like the mark left by someone in a chair.

I dream about the train again and the walkway to the station from the shopping centre. It's narrow and if it's busy it's slow with crowds but if you're alone each step reverberates as the walkway bounces but in a crowd the vibration absorbed by bodies. But anyway I'm late or I have the wrong ticket or something and anyway I go down onto the platform and there are two trains. I don't know which to choose and anyway they're already leaving the station usually slowly. And I can catch one but the steps are high and it's difficult to get into a carriage or the door won't open but I cling to the outside of the carriage or sometimes I get inside and it leaves the station very slowly. Only half a mile outside the station I know it's the wrong train so I get out and run back toward the station so I don't miss the right train of course I never get there or I do and the whole thing happens over again.

(The man said do you have a ticket? the first time and I said I was late for work and rushed through because there was a queue and is it ok if I pay now and I did and it was as much as the ticket would have been for a few days but I reckon I broke even because mostly I didn't pay and I don't know if I enjoyed the thing that flooded through me or if it was shame. The second time I did a whole pantomime of searching through my bag and the second guy let me off but I felt more dishonest about it though both times had been a lie.)

It's there but it's not there.

(That last bit was not a dream it was real.)

September

Type

The course starts in September, like school. If university doesn't work out you have this to fall back on. My mother says.

Beginning to need a jumper in the evenings.

To sit in at the front of a classroom, still summer heat at midday, with other people I can't see. I think they are all girls. The desks are long benches with black tops so the machines don't slip. We type all together with the left hand:
fdf
FDF

My parents sit inside now. They watch a crime drama. Someone is being killed in the woods.

No that's right they are all women, mostly older, mostly not going to university or never having gone or sometimes saying they can go or that they went and are going back or sometimes that they are not going back or sometimes going back sometime and anyway I mean they not much older than me but not girls, women. The college is on the ring road. I could get the bus to the New Town, it's closer, but I get the bus from the Old Town, I can walk from there.

Yes I know it is a woman. It always is.

Then with the right hand:

jkj

JKJ

The year is closing now.

There is a name for this weather: dull. Everything hits, metallic, against the sky. Thud.

The sky is too thick to get through. It is low. This is the sky now for the rest of the year. I'd forgotten what it was like.

Then with each hand in turn:

FDF

Jkj

fdf

JKJ

The sky, white.

Things are going to seed.

No.

The seeds have left.

The plants curl up and die.

(Curl up and Dye! The name of the hairdresser in the Old Town!)

Then with both hands at the same time:

Fsf

Jlj

Frf

juj

The first cold morning my body shrinks I mean my fingers, my thighs more narrow not pressed against my jeans not melting against each other but hard discrete. It is a warning.

Nature is full of warnings. Red is a warning.

A ladybird is poisonous. But ripe things are red too.

It's difficult to know when to be scared.

KiK

kIk

DeD

dEd

sfs

Ljl

Red if you look the tips of the thorns on the rosehips, the tips of the hawthorn leaves spreading upward from the tips of the branches. But red's fake, temporary. What lives here's brown. All the year round.

ffff dddd ssss aaaa ffff dddd ssss aaaa ffff dddd ssss aaaa

Everything is too heavy now, the green collapsing on itself. Briars, the blackberries hard knots something rotten white, lye on them hard, the hawthorn full red.

fdsa fdsa fdsa fdsa fdsa fdsa fdsa fdsa fdsa fdsa

The knots of green full red.
Elsewhere the bones of earlier plants.
Something is always surviving.

jjjj kkkk llll ;;;; jjjj kkkk llll ;;;; jjjj kkkk llll ;;;;

They have made themselves survive this year. That's what summer is. That's
what it does. It looks like rest but it's work.

asdf asdf asdf asdf asdf asdf asdf asdf asdf asdf

The days are escaping. I do the same thing over. They still don't hang together.
They're so boring. They can't go quick enough. What can I make of them?

jkl; jkl; jkl; jkl; jkl; jkl; jkl; jkl; jkl; jkl; jkl; jkl;

Fall back.
(Clocks. Soon.)

The trick is not to look down at your hands.

If it survives it rots.

Key

I have to give Rosemary back her spare key. If I keep it, it burns.
Remember

I don't know what happened. But something has happened.
Let me tell you.
In any case I put some time between.

I didn't want to phone. Or I did and there was no one there. Or I did
and I didn't leave a message. Or if I left a message, I don't remember. Or
if I didn't. I didn't want to leave another message. Once Rosemary had
said come over any time. And she gave me her key.

In the meantime my grandmother is dead.
(Did someone cut her toenails?)

Rosemary's dad has a phone with no curly cord. It does not have
a dial but buttons. It has a little prick hard in the corner with a knob-
end on top that sends a signal back to the box. We have a phone with a
curly cord your fingers ache from dialling sometimes it catches them at
the first joint as you drag them round. I know how long it takes to dial
Rosemary's number. I know what Rosemary's phone looks like when
it's ringing.

Which were yellow. Of course, after we do not see them.

She is in a coffin lined with something white edged with lace like the doll's cot I had. Over her legs something wood, a half-door, a car bonnet—

I went back to give Rosemary her key. I'd picked some flowers from the gardens past the ring road. I let myself in with the key, and left it, the key and the flowers no note, I didn't know what to say.

—no one sleeps like that in life—

When I went in someone was there. I don't know who. Perhaps it was me. I didn't see anything. Or what I saw I can't say. I can tell it was something I shouldn't say to anyone so all the time I saw it I kept my eyes tight shut even though they were open you can do that you know if you try to focus broadly focus on everything at once so you're looking at everything all the same time or sort of draw your eyes into yourself like what's in front of you isn't happening and to refuse to relate each action even if you can see everything quite clearly. This isn't the same as seeing. I stood there for a moment doing that.

—her eyes closed so she couldn't see how it was for us to see her.

It was me who shouldn't have been seen.

So we couldn't see how she looked at us seeing.

I went without being seen. Was it Rosemary saw me? She did not say she saw me. When I saw her next she didn't say she'd seen me. She didn't ask for her key back. I only saw her across the road.

I remember the doll in the cot very well. Her plastic smelt so good: lime, play-

186

doh, dirt. She was perfect. She was given me at my other grandad's funeral. I was too young to go. She was not a baby doll but a doll of a girl the age I was then. She has not grown like me. She smelt how my body should smell.

I don't know what I saw but it is something I continue not to put into words. Or was it that I was seen. Who was intruding on whom?

In both cases—on the doll and in the coffin—the lace was broderie anglaise.

Let's have no words of this.
But when they ask you what it means, say,
Thank you.

When you tipped back the doll so she's lying down, her eyes closed.

We didn't do anything.
(What was not done was bad enough.)
I had one chance to tell this tale. So I don't tell it.
No need to tell. I don't go back again.

One day I picked off her nylon eyelashes to see if I could see the mechanism. I couldn't but her lids closed just the same, only a sliver between.

(This coda seems extraneous. Still, it is what I did.)

Because she no longer had eyelashes I do not have the doll any more.

I could tell this many times. However many times I tell it I still don't know what anything means.

Country

The country is another past. Things were done differently to them there. Only the country, that is. In town the past is circled by the present, or rather the recent present which is beginning to look a little like the past, its concrete cracked. Or rather. The country's not timeless not like they say. Did you know there were more creatures once, before the sprays and? There were more songbirds, for instance? And also plants between. There was also famine failure flood diseases that killed you quick-not-slow, so take your pick. The country is not the past. It is not the present. The past the present are our things and it resists us. One day after us there is the country again. Not this country farmed but the hills. Even now when it rains you think it's paleolithic not a single living human, no town certainly. The country is not the past. The country is the future.

I am not going to the town any more.

Veronica

There is a new girl called Veronica from the typing class.

The fields, apprehensive. Already trimmed. Waiting.

I mean she is not new.
I mean I didn't notice her before.

Not wet but cold. You don't want to go in but you do.
Inside. Shadows. Things in real 3d form. Not proper inside yet but everything
how it is the rest of the year.

Inside in 3d we escape, watching 2d.
Our rooms so boxlike.
Or, indeed, we look only toward the corners. If not the screen where
else can we look?
What happened two weeks ago?
(Rosemary's party.)
These interiors barely exist.

Cold in the morning now. The day heats up but. Things putting covers
round themselves: cobwebs, egg-sacs. All these covers are filmy, all white, all soft.
Fruits withdraw into the husks of flowers, withered brown dry. If I am going into
something similar but I don't know: a world of people I mean in a set a hive where
you have your place with them and out of nature. I can see it but I can't see it. I

189

mean I can't see their faces. I don't know them yet.

I no longer know if adult woman is a blue suit.

The typing women do not wear them.

Inside looks always the same. Outside is changing all the time. You can replay the rest on video.

I know how to set the timer.

The butterflies ragged. A frog with only one back leg. Somehow things survive. Even here.

Veronica is in her garden.

I don't see her. I don't see her red hair which I can see if she is there.

Or maybe they breed like that.

In the village on the lawns in the big houses, only the garden furniture.

In the small back gardens fences; drives in front, gardens behind.

In the big houses in which gardens all around

Veronica.

Old man's beard, peeling off. Everything has an inside. It's white. Suddenly you see it. Other things are stripped off, white inside everything.

Veronica says if you breathe in and hold it then you are pushed hard against a wall, you faint.

She said they tried it at school.

She pushes me hard against the door, then I push her.

We don't faint.

Veronica went to the private school.

I have never tried this before.

Rose Bay Willow Herb. That liberal shepherds. Like a man, white seeds in something fluid, so we've been told. The microscope close-ups. Old man's beard, the seeds in air: gross. You can't get away from them.

The boys on the private school bus sing:

—It would take a coal miner to find her vagina

And the hairs on her dicky di do hang down to her knees.

One black one, one white one

and one with a bit of shite on,

and one with a fairy light on,

TO SHOW US THE WAY!—

This is the year they let girls into the VIth form.

Veronica was one of them.

Everywhere a little death.

In Veronica's VIth form they are doing a play from Shakespeare. I go with her because I am reading Shakespeare.

It is all boys.

In the play some girls dress up as boys for disguise. But they're boys anyway. Someone said that's how they did it in Shakespeare's time so that's why it's right not to have girls now.

What is the difference between living and surviving?

In Veronica's front room, on the telly an ad: someone says, *it's good to talk.*

The hanging trees explode very slow across the sky red now.
It takes them an entire year.

Veronica's dad brings airport trays. He is a pilot.
We eat fish fingers in one section, beans in another.
Veronica says, let's eat them in front of the telly. This is not generally allowed.
Veronica is happy but I don't like to be eating like a baby. Because her dad is a pilot, I try to feel I am wrong.

Some strange white flowers like campions. Did they stray here from some garden?

On the telly an ad: *how much you eat in a year.* Am I so much? This is information I don't know what to do with. Is there anything I can do to not be that much?

The cold that comes down. Is that dew? About 9pm. Sitting outside. Like someone's turned the air on.

I cannot eat any more from the tray.
Veronica is not Rosemary, but I am willing to make the adjustment.

Through

And finally someone came through the glass door. When I got home it was smashed.

I got home first before anyone. I had been at the typing school.

What does rape smell of? Something already going off. The fields breathed it. Now it is gone.

From the stream I can hear dogs barking across the valley.

I walked into the house through the back door. That's where I usually go in. I only notice when I got to the front, glass inside the house on top of the letters on top of the doormat, the thickness of each piece of glass, I hadn't known how thick, glass that was neither outside nor inside in pieces now outside and inside, in both of the places it is supposed not to.

At first I can't think where it came from.

On this side of the valley a dog answers. Too quickly. But it doesn't, really.

(I do not leave the house straight away though later they tell me that's what I should have done. No, I walk up the stairs. The house, for the first time, feels mine.)

Is it sulphur? Is sulphur something I can say I've smelt? It smells like eggs, right? Rosemary smells of eggshells, her sister of the promise of sulphur.

Only the rape smells properly of sulphur.

The rape and eggs.

The drawers are all pulled out my mother's drawers with her falsies and her crotchless bras, my father's drawers with his underpants that are made of string and his vests folded like soft skin her wardrobe open with the dresses splayed out in surprising colours flame red turquoise jacquard polyester, my father's dusty black and his ties engaged on the floor.

I went to her jewellery box.

In the fields, bales, harvested. They smell of urine. It makes you press your legs together. Me, I mean. Does no one else notice that?

Is there anything missing? I know there is a string of brown wood beads, oval and light, that smell of something very of old: wood but not quite, broken.

I pick up:
a strapless bra.
the ties, a bright tangle.
When you put clothes on they look very different to when they lie there.

Oats in the wild grass, unharvested, have hairs like on Rosemary. Walking through the grass they catch my legs. The hairs on the oats sting, but not unpleasantly.

In my room nothing disturbed. What did it look there to take? Only one cupboard door open. My window looks onto the sunset.

It sees no one out there.

And they are the same colour: blonde.

Downstairs. I open the patio doors. They slide and catch on their fur tracks.

I go back to the hall and stand by the telephone table. Its seat covered with glass.

I ring Rosemary's mother's number. Then her father's. No one answers.

I call my mother's work. She tells me to get out.

I waited by the underpass by

S

E

X

until she gets home.

(The French window loose all the time but they did not know they could get in there with no bother.)

I like that something sticks to me.

The policeman comes in to question us while we are watching the telly. I only feel what comes through the door is a man. *Daddy,* I say, *we're watching Countdown.*

I know they only feel sticky and in fact they have small barbs.

If anyone was there I didn't hear them.

Sentence

I am working toward a sentence that can say everything at once. I think I can make one but not yet about the valley and the town all in the same sentence and about now and about what has been everything I remember and what the valley remembers a sentence that takes into account each blade of grass—yes the topside that flashes white and the underside that is deep blue the smell when you walk on it—and the same for all the stems of wheat that catch the sun all together like they're one thing like a giant metal monster and the fields at all the times of year all together the fields liquid green the gold the stubble that sticks out of the ground the straw on the roads the smell of fields burnt thick like tar hanging in the air their colour deeper than anything still not black as nothing's black in nature only words and there is no need for prepositions because everything is at the same time and in the same place there are lots of verbs lots of doing words but layered on top of each other like people all speaking at once. It is like how time crosses the valley like i.e. the wind that puts its shape into things always everywhere at the same time like what I said about the shape in the settee I mean sofa i.e. it's invisible but is the past and the present at the same time.

It takes less than one second to say.
I do not know how long it takes to write.

I can't make any sentence about the future. I don't know if I can make one about anything outside the valley.

Hamlet

The man who comes into the garden while I am reading Hamlet is a religious man. He has no books. He may have leaflets but he does not show them to me.

I am reading Hamlet because I am going to university. It is not Rosemary's university, but it is a university and I am going. So I must read it on my own.

There is no water in the stream. Anyhow I don't go to the stream much any more.

I do not relax outside anyway. I only try to look like I am relaxing. Because this is a garden.
I am outside. A man has come into the garden. It has happened.

(The thing the bird the sounds like something metal being hit. At the same time like it's swallowing its sound. What is it? Garden bird, a blackbird maybe?)

The day is undecided.

What did I say to him? I can't remember now. Something Ophelia said.

Further along the channel, grasses grow to the height of three feet. The river bed looks like a ditch along the field. Only it winds.

In the field next door, the roofs' ribs are up.
The builders are not there.
What does relaxing look like?

I dig into the stream bed with sticks and there is wet sand but water does not come out.

The workmen are gone.
The houses have empty windows.

By whom am I worried I am looked at?
The man who came into the garden said, *I think you mean Hamlet.*

Let me tell you.

In school we did 'roofs' or 'rooves' but that was years ago when the lesson smelt of my mother's necklace. It is a nice old smell like wood. I cannot smell the smell again. Only almost. The necklace is gone now. And I cannot remember the right answer.
I cannot remember the right answer for the man.
Rosemary, remember,
You should not have believed me.

Everything being really still in the garden this evening, I mean that's unusual, not how nature is: the leaves of the sycamore so big and heavy, I mean sculptural, I guess that's what I mean. And gesturing dramatically,

like I don't know what like someone imitating a statue, moving, not like
a statue at all then—

Do you doubt that?

I can now say I want to have sex.
I don't not think this conflicts with my habit of being alone.

The oats are still in the fields. They turn over like a body.

Having just finished reading a play called *Ophelia*.
Having just left off from where I was.
(Still being here.)
Looked up.

I think nothing.

(The leaves are still green. And this is at the beginning of summer.)

End

Rosemary's sister brings cigarettes down to the river.
The end of hers glows hot. You can see it from the ridge.
If there are two, that means Rosemary is there also.
It is past the end of the holidays. The cattery is empty.
It is dark by the stream because the stream is in a valley. The sun sets across the ridge. It is light there.
The sun sets early now.
You can still see the cigarette.

We never saw any farmers in the fields.
We saw only their machines.

If I ride into the village, past the church.

The water has come back to the river.

The inside of Rosemary's sister's pants is stained yellow-green.
I understand now that this is cystitis.
Rosemary's mother doesn't speak to me 'confidentially' any more.

They still burn the fields.

When there are two red cigarette glows, it means Rosemary *and* her sister.

But there is only one glow.

We take off our clothes to go into the river.

The fields are black.

When it is dark the river is colder.

Only Rosemary's sister.

She has cigarettes.

When it is cold, the river is darker.

The men have not come back to the building site. They have not been there for a month.

Rosemary's sister also brings a radio to the river.

The absence of Rosemary is hot and dark.

Her sister is cool and smooth. We say little to one another.

We can see nothing in the water, not even our bodies.

Most of the walls are up. The roofs are ribs. The windows are empty.

Nevertheless it is still summer

(Because we say that to each other).

We adjust the frequency. The radio crackles. No one comes, no cars.

It is early. But it is dark.

I can see down into them from my bedroom.

There are no interior walls.

The fish have gone. Or maybe they were frogs.

I don't know what happens outside the valley.

The stream is deeper and moves again, and stuff browns in it, new stuff. Green.

Even now.

I still think of Rosemary at some point every day.

I don't know what we have done all summer.

It is easy to get through our fence. You can walk inside the empty houses, or around them.

At least I think of doing that but I don't do it.

I never do what I think about.

In October I go to university with my man's mouth.

All my life, I don't hear from Rosemary again.

Acknowledgements

Thank you to Visual Editions for publishing the original Seed app at seed-story.com, to Google Creative Lab for bringing the structure I'd imagined to life, and to Charlotte Hicks for her illustrations. Thank you to my PhD supervisors at the University of East Anglia, Jeremy Noel-Tod and Clare Connors. Thank you to Arts Council England for supporting the development of the performance version of this text, to Simon Thorne and Samuel Barnes for designing the soundtrack, and to all the women volunteers who took part in the performances. And thank you to David, Emma and Stephen at No Alibis Press for imagining a print edition, and for making it happen.